MORE
OF T

OTHER TITLES OF INTEREST

MORE ADVANCED USES
OF THE MULTIMETER

by
R. A. PENFOLD

BERNARD BABANI (publishing) LTD
THE GRAMPIANS
SHEPHERDS BUSH ROAD
LONDON W6 7NF
ENGLAND

PLEASE NOTE

Although every care has been taken with the production of this book to ensure that any projects, designs, modifications and/or programs etc. contained herewith, operate in a correct and safe manner and also that any components specified are normally available in Great Britain, the Publishers do not accept responsibility in any way for the failure, including fault in design, of any project, design, modification or program to work correctly or to cause damage to any other equipment that it may be connected to or used in conjunction with, or in respect of any other damage or injury that may be so caused, nor do the Publishers accept responsibility in any way for the failure to obtain specified components.

Notice is also given that if equipment that is still under warranty is modified in any way or used or connected with home-built equipment then that warranty may be void.

© 1989 BERNARD BABANI (publishing) LTD

First Published — October 1989

British Library Cataloguing in Publication Data
Penfold, R. A.
    More advance uses of the multimeter.
    1. Multimeters. Use
    I. Title
    621.3815'48

ISBN 0 85934 210 7

Printed and Bound in Great Britain by Cox & Wyman Ltd, Reading

Preface

"Getting The Most From Your Multimeter" (BP239) covers the basics of multimeters and how they are used in fault finding on electronic projects. This book carries on where BP239 left off, and it is assumed that readers are either familiar with the earlier book, or are otherwise conversant with basic test procedures using a multimeter. Although you need a certain amount of technical knowledge in order to fully exploit the information in this publication, you do not need a really indepth knowledge of electronics.

Some simple component testing procedures are covered in BP239, and this theme is taken up here in chapter 1 which covers some quick and simple methods of component testing plus some suggestions for detailed testing of certain types of component. Checking integrated circuits is often difficult without the aid of special test equipment of the type used by component manufacturers, but the simple techniques described here enable a wide range of integrated circuits to at least be given some basic checks, and comprehensive methods of testing are provided for some popular types of integrated circuit.

Although a multimeter is a supremely versatile piece of test equipment, it is not without its "blind spots". Chapter 2 covers some useful but simple and inexpensive add-ons that extend the capabilities of a multimeter. These include a.c. and d.c. booster amplifiers, memory circuits, and a current tracer add-on.

R. A. Penfold

Contents

Chapter 1

COMPONENT TESTING

Component testing is a subject that was covered in "Getting The Most From Your Multimeter" (BP239) in some detail. In fact the whole of chapter 2 in BP239 is devoted to the subject of component checking. Here we will consider this important topic in some detail again, carrying on from where BP239 left off. We will be concerned with the testing of components that were not covered in BP239, as well as more advanced methods of testing components that were covered by this earlier book. We will also look at a few quick but effective test methods that are not covered in BP239. These include a quick method of checking transistors.

Unijunction Transistors

There seems to be few new circuits these days that utilize a unijunction transistor. These components offer a very simple means of producing an audio or infra-audio oscillator, timing circuit, etc., but have been largely ousted by the 555 timer integrated circuit and the low power versions of that device. These offer better predictability and reliability, as well as being much more versatile. However, from time to time you may still find yourself building a project that uses one of these devices, particularly if you indulge in the increasingly popular pastime of building projects from old publications. Also, you may need to deal with one of these components if a project built some years ago should develop a fault. These devices once appeared in electronic projects for the home constructor almost as frequently as the 555 and its derivatives do today.

Internally, a unijunction transistor effectively consists of two resistors and a silicon diode connected in the arrangement shown in Figure 1.1. Note that connecting two resistors and a silicon diode in this configuration will not give you a circuit that will properly mimic a unijunction transistor. In its most common role as a relaxation oscillator, a unijunction transistor operates in a circuit of the type shown in Figure 1.2. Initially the single semiconductor junction (from which the device

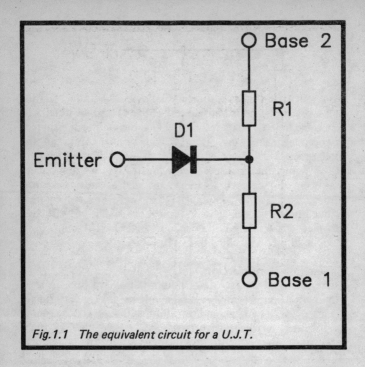

Fig.1.1 The equivalent circuit for a U.J.T.

derives its name) is reverse biased, and C1 is able to charge up via R1. This continues until the charge voltage reaches about 0.6 volts more than the voltage at the junction of the internal potential divider of the unijunction. The semiconductor junction (i.e. the diode of Figure 1.1) then becomes forward biased. This results in a regenerative action within the device that causes its base 1 to base 2 resistance to drop to a very low level.

This has several effects, one of which is to rapidly discharge C1 via the emitter – base 1 terminals of the unijunction and the low resistance of R3. This regenerative action does not occur if you use two resistors and a diode in a unijunction style circuit, and it is for this reason that a proper unijunction device is needed in order to get this type of oscillator to function properly. When the charge on C1 reaches a low level, the discharge current becomes too low to maintain the regenerative action, the unijunction switches off, and C1 starts to

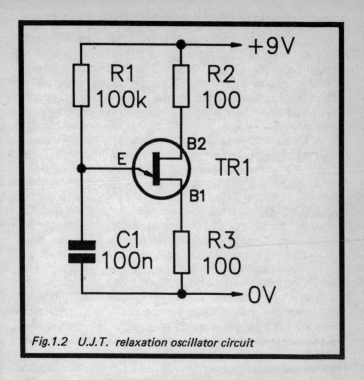

Fig.1.2   U.J.T. relaxation oscillator circuit

charge up again via R1. This action continues indefinitely. Pulse signals are generated across R2 and R3 due to one of the internal resistors of the unijunction effectively becoming a short circuit while the device is in the triggered state. This reduces the base 1 to base 2 resistance of the component, giving an increase in the voltage across the two base load resistors. There is also a non-linear sawtooth waveform (at what is often quite a high impedance) generated across C1.

Probably the best method of checking a unijunction transistor is to connect it into a relaxation oscillator such as the one shown in Figure 1.2. It should not take more than a minute to breadboard a simple circuit of this type. You will need some means of detecting the audio output signal, but something as basic as a crystal earphone will suffice. If a relaxation oscillator of this type fails to oscillate it is often due to unsuitable component values rather than what could genuinely be considered a fault in the unijunction transistor. With some circuits a wide range of frequencies have to be covered in a single range. This requires the use of a variable timing resistance which might have a minimum resistance of just a few kilohms running through to a maximum resistance that could be as high as a few megohms. If the timing resistance is made too low, the result is that the current through R1 is high enough to hold the unijunction in the "on" state. This will clearly prevent oscillation from occurring. The result will be much the same if the timing resistance is too high, but with leakage currents preventing the device from triggering. If the device is held in the triggered state the measured voltage across C1 will be quite low, but if it is failing to trigger, the voltage across C1 will probably be 50% or more of the supply voltage (but you will need a high impedance voltmeter to stand any chance of getting an accurate reading).

If you find that oscillation cuts off with a variable frequency oscillator of this type adjusted well towards one or other end of its frequency range, this almost certainly indicates a problem with the timing resistance becoming too high or too low for the particular unijunction in use. Under these circumstances the only way of obtaining satisfactory results might be to try a new unijunction transistor in the circuit. This problem can also occur with fixed frequency oscillators where it has been necessary to use a very high or very low timing resistance for some reason. It might then be possible to obtain correct operation of the circuit by making the timing resistance lower and the timing capacitance higher, or the timing resistance higher and the timing capacitance lower, as appropriate. Provided any change in the value of one is matched by a proportional but opposite change in the other, the operating frequency of the circuit should remain unchanged.

If the timing resistor and capacitor are both very high in value, bear in mind that any lack of oscillation can be due to leakage in the capacitor. The same is also true of timer circuits that use a simple C – R timing network, and it is something that can afflict any timing circuit which uses a high value resistor and capacitor, not just unijunction circuits. What happens in these cases is that at some point the leakage current through the capacitor becomes equal to the charge current through the resistor. At this point the charge voltage ceases to rise, and the trigger point of the unijunction (or whatever) is never reached.

It is not practical to check for this problem by simply measuring the voltage across the timing capacitor to see if it has stopped rising. The current tapped off by the multimeter, even if it is a digital type with a resistance of about ten or eleven megohms, could well be high enough to ensure that the charge voltage would stop rising before the trigger potential is reached. Using the multimeter set to a high resistance range to make a leakage check on the timing capacitor is a more reliable method of checking for this problem. For satisfactory results to be obtained the leakage resistance of the capacitor would need to be about double the value of the timing resistor, and quite probably much higher in value than this. If a timing circuit or low frequency oscillator is unreliable or inconsistent in performance, this is usually indicative of problems with excessive leakage in the timing capacitor.

Capacitor leakage is a very common problem with simple timer circuits and very low frequency oscillators. Where possible use a non-electrolytic capacitor. The high values involved sometimes make this impractical, but tantalum bead capacitors often offer a solution to the problem. Failing that, an electrolytic component sold as a "low leakage" type should be used. Avoid very cheap or old components in critical applications such as this, as they often have very high leakage levels.

Transistor Resistance Checks
You can make a rough check on a unijunction device by making some resistance checks between its terminals. Data for unijunction transistors will specify the base 1 to base 2 resistance (the "RBB" parameter), and this can obviously be checked without any difficulty. This resistance is usually a few kilohms, and is between 4k7 and 9k1 for the popular 2N2646 unijunction for example.

From the emitter to either of the base terminals a diode action should be obtained, although the forward resistance

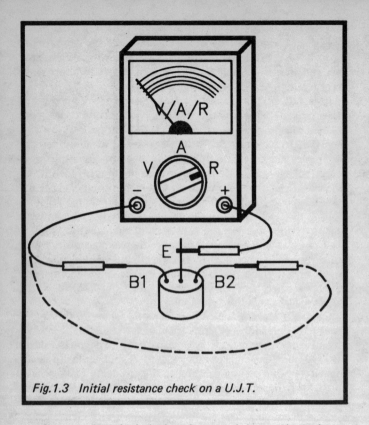

Fig.1.3   Initial resistance check on a U.J.T.

reading may be a little higher than usual due to the inclusion of about half the base 1 to base 2 resistance in series with the diode. In fact the deflection of the meter's pointer may be very small if you use a low resistance range. One having a centre scale reading of about 20k or more should be about right. Unijunction transistors are not usually symmetrical, and the emitter to base 1 resistance is likely to be a little higher than the emitter to base 2 resistance. Figures 1.3 and 1.4 show how to make these emitter — base checks, and the results that should be obtained.

If you are using a digital multimeter rather than an analogue type, remember that the test prods for each test must be

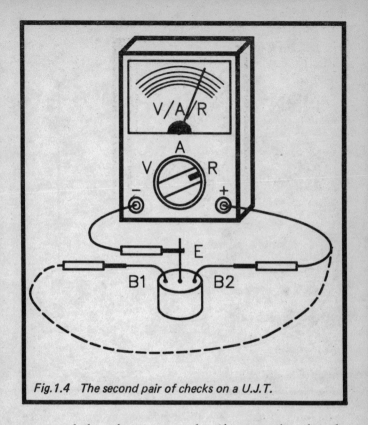

Fig.1.4   The second pair of checks on a U.J.T.

connected the other way round. Also remember that the test must be undertaken using the meter set to the "hi" setting, where appropriate, so that the test voltage is high enough to forward bias the semiconductor junction. This warning should also be heeded when making the resistance checks on semiconductor junctions that are described later in this chapter.

This general method of checking unijunction transistors can be modified and used as a quick method of checking bipolar devices. The equivalent circuit of a bipolar transistor is a pair of back-to-back diodes connected as shown in Figure 1.5. As can be seen from this diagram, the polarity of the diodes is different for n.p.n. and p.n.p. devices.

7

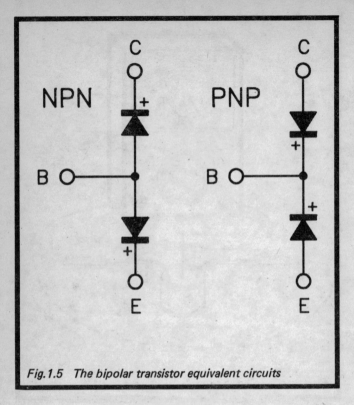

Fig.1.5   The bipolar transistor equivalent circuits

In order to test a transistor it is merely necessary to make some resistance checks across pairs of contacts in order to make sure that the correct diode actions are obtained. First the pair of checks detailed in Figure 1.6 should be made. This reverse biases the two diode junctions in turn, and should give an extremely high reading in both cases (probably an infinite reading). The next test (which is shown in Figure 1.7) forward biases both diode junctions, and should give the low resistance readings normally associated with a forward biased silicon junction. The final pair of tests are shown in Figure 1.8, and they check for a very high resistance between the collector and emitter terminals, regardless of which way round the test prods are connected. For both n.p.n. and p.n.p. devices the

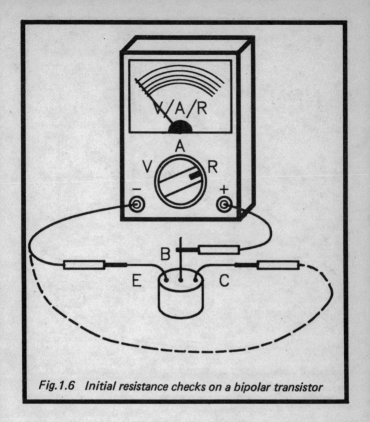

Fig.1.6 Initial resistance checks on a bipolar transistor

two diodes are connected with the opposite polarity, and whichever way round the test prods are connected, one or other of these diodes will block the current flow.

The checks in Figures 1.6 to 1.8 are for an n.p.n. test transistor, but the same method of testing can be applied to p.n.p. devices. However, the setup of Figure 1.6 will give low readings, while that of Figure 1.7 will give very high readings. As pointed out previously, the tests of Figure 1.8 should produce high readings for either type of transistor.

Simple static tests of this type are obviously not 100% reliable. A device could pass these tests but still be deficient in some way. However, in practice a transistor which passes

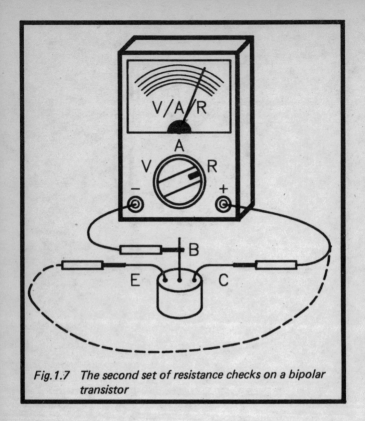

Fig.1.7 The second set of resistance checks on a bipolar transistor

these tests is very likely to be fully serviceable, and not the cause of a fault. Things are more clear cut if a device fails one of these tests. If this should happen, there is very little chance of the component being fully functional. I will not say that it is impossible for a transistor to fail one of these checks and still be operational, but on the face of it this would seem to be totally impossible.

Another use of these tests is in finding out whether a transistor is an n.p.n. or p.n.p. device. It can also help to determine which lead is which on a device of unknown type number. This can be useful when trying to sort out what's what in a bargain pack of "untested" transistors or "tested but

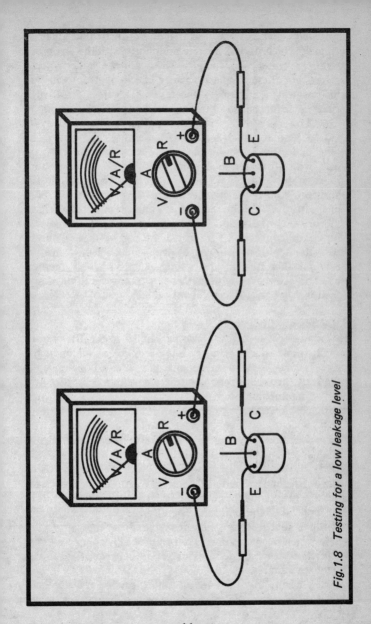

Fig. 1.8   Testing for a low leakage level

unmarked" devices. First use trial and error to find a pair of terminals which do not provide continuity with the test prods connected either way round. These are the collector and emitter, but these simple resistance checks will not tell you which is which. Then try the tests of Figure 1.6. If high resistance readings are obtained, the test device is an n.p.n. type. Low resistance readings show that it is a p.n.p. type.

To determine which leadout is the emitter and which one is the collector, try subjecting the device to a current gain check with these terminals connected first one way round, and then the other. With one method of connection the transistor should provide a healthy level of current gain, while with the opposite method of connection it should have little or no current gain. Obviously the former is the correct method of connection. Provided the test voltage is only a few volts there is no real risk of damaging a silicon transistor by connecting it with the wrong polarity. This method would be a bit risky with germanium transistors though, and it is probably best not to try it with these.

S.C.R.s and I.C.s

This method of testing can also be applied to S.C.R.s — both thyristors and triacs. A thyristor is a four layer semiconductor which, as far as static resistance checks are concerned, is effectively two transistors connected as shown in Figure 1.9. Both transistors are normally switched off, giving a very high resistance between the anode and cathode terminals, regardless of which way round the test prods are connected. The gate and cathode terminals are effectively the base and emitter terminals of an n.p.n. transistor, and as such provide a diode action. In fact when subjected to resistance checks, a thyristor behaves in almost exactly the same way as an n.p.n. transistor, with the gate, anode, and cathode respectively acting as the base, collector, and emitter. There is one difference though, and this is that there is a high resistance from the gate to the anode whichever way round the test prods are connected. An n.p.n. transistor provides a diode action between its base and collector terminals.

Once again, this method of testing can be used to help identify the terminals of a device which has an unknown

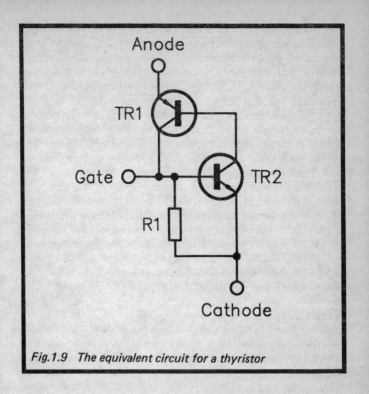

Fig.1.9 The equivalent circuit for a thyristor

leadout configuration. Use trial and error to find two terminals that provide a diode action. These are the gate and cathode terminals, and from the polarity of the junction you can deduce which is which. The other terminal is obviously the anode.

Results are similar if a triac is tested using the same resistance checks, but with the MT2 terminal taking the place of the anode, and the MT1 terminal taking the place of the cathode. However, as a triac is a bidirectional device, its gate to MT1 terminals will act as a forward biased diode whichever way round the test prods are connected. This complicates matters if you use these tests in an attempt to identify the leadouts of a device which has an unknown leadout configuration. There is no way of ascertaining which is the gate and which is the MT1 terminal since there is continuity between

13

these terminals with the test prods connected either way round.

Integrated Circuits

Integrated circuits are notoriously difficult to test. As we shall see shortly, it is possible to test some of the more simple analogue and digital devices by rigging up a basic test circuit and making a few voltage checks. This approach is inapplicable to many integrated circuits though, as their functions are far too complex to be tested in such a fundamental manner. It is possible to apply resistance checks to integrated circuits though, and in many cases this will produce useful results. The only problem in using this type of testing is that the complexity of many integrated circuits makes it difficult to determine what sort of resistance readings should be present between any two given terminals. Being realistic about it, the only way of overcoming this problem is to make checks on a device that is known to be fully functioning, so that you have something against which tests made on a suspect device (or devices) can be made.

There is a potential flaw in this system in that much of the circuitry in an integrated circuit is well removed from any of the pins. A major fault in a part of the circuit that only connects to one of the pins via a very indirect route may not show up in resistance checks. In practice a lot of faults in integrated circuits occur due to excessive input and output currents, or similar problems, and the damaged circuitry will be in parts of the device which connect directly to one or more of its pins. Also, where a breakdown does occur somewhere in the middle of a complex integrated circuit, the result is often a chain fault which results in much of the circuit being destroyed. This is likely to show up quite clearly on resistance checks. You still need to bear in mind that resistance checks on semiconductor devices are not totally conclusive. If a device passes the checks it could still be below specification. If a device fails a test, then it is almost certainly a "dud".

Testing the resistance from every pin to every other pin of an integrated circuit, with the test prods connected both ways round, is probably not a practical proposition. Even with an eight or fourteen pin device it could take quite a long time, and with a forty pin integrated circuit it would take an inordinate amount of time. Probably the best approach is to measure the resistance between the 0 volt supply pin and every other pin, and then repeat the procedure with the test prods reversed. Obviously you will not be able to memorise the results of numerous resistance checks, and will have to write down the test results obtained from the standard device against which others will be judged. A simple chart, as in the example shown here, is probably the best way of writing down your results.

Pin Number	Negative Prod To 0 Volt	Positive Prod To 0 Volt
1	5.5k	500k
2	5.5k	500k
3	4.5k	500k
4	5.5k	500k
5	4.5k	500k
6	5.5k	500k
7	4.5k	500k
8	5.5k	500k
9	4.5k	500k
10	0 Volt Pin	0 Volt Pin
11	5.5k	500k
12	4.5k	500k
13	5.5k	500k
14	4.5k	500k
15	5.5k	500k
16	4.5k	500k
17	5.5k	500k
18	4.5k	500k
19	5.5k	500k
20	3.5k	180k

Dangers

There are a few points to keep in mind when trying this type of testing. One is that it works better with bipolar integrated circuits than it does with CMOS, NMOS, or PMOS types. It will actually work quite well with these MOS integrated

15

circuits, but only if they have pull-up resistors on the inputs. What can happen otherwise is that stray and varying voltages on the inputs result in the resistance readings you obtain varying over wide limits. This obviously makes a set of test results of dubious worth, and difficult to take anyway.

Another point about MOS devices which do not have pull-up resistors at inputs, or some other effective form of static protection, is that they are vulnerable to damage due to static charges. Making measurements on a device which is out of circuit and not in its protective packaging is a bit risky, especially if it is a highly complex and costly component. There are ways of reducing the risk, one of which is to fit the test component onto a breadboard which is wired so that each pin of the device is connected to a common "earth" rail via a high value resistor (around 5.6 to 10 megohms should suffice). This should prevent any large voltage build-ups on the pins so that the device is kept safe. It should also prevent any stray voltages reaching sufficient amplitude to operate any of the inputs, and in this way the varying readings mentioned previously are avoided. It is a good idea to fit the test device onto a breadboard anyway. You can then use a short piece of wire and a crocodile clip lead to make the connection to the 0 volt pin of the device, leaving both hands free to connect the other test prod to the remaining pins and to note down results.

Another method of protecting static sensitive devices is to push their pins into a piece of conductive foam (the black foam material in which many integrated circuits are supplied these days). In my experience this material does not conduct particularly well, and it will not have a significant affect on the resistance readings. This method has the disadvantage that it is a little slower and more difficult to make the connections to the pins and note down the results.

When checking delicate integrated circuits you must be careful about the choice of measuring range. A low range is undesirable as it could produce quite large current flows that could damage the test components. A high resistance range is not a good choice as the test voltage could be high enough to damage the test components (but this depends on the type and model of multimeter in use). A range having a mid-scale value of about 20k should be suitable. When testing very delicate devices it is probably best to only take measurements with the positive test prod (or negative prod of a digital instrument) connected to the 0 volt supply pin. This avoids applying a voltage of the wrong polarity to the other pins of the device.

Wherever possible, the best method of testing any complex integrated circuit is to plug it into a circuit that is known to be fully functioning, and then see if the device functions properly in this circuit. However, in practice this might not be too easy to achieve. Very often you will not know for certain whether the main circuit is alright and the integrated circuit is at fault, or vice versa, or perhaps they are both faulty. Plugging a new integrated circuit into part of a circuit that does not seem to be functioning properly may seem to be the obvious course of action, but do not be in too much of a hurry to plug an expensive integrated circuit into a circuit board that caused the demise of the original integrated circuit, as fitting a replacement device could just lead to this new component being instantly "zapped" at switch-on! If you think you have located a faulty integrated circuit, it is always a good idea to make a few checks to determine whether or not there is a fault on the board which caused the damage to the device. Integrated circuits are very reliable, and failures are often due to something like an excessive supply voltage due to a power supply fault.

I.C. Test Circuits

Rigging up a breadboarded test circuit for a complex integrated circuit will usually be an impractical proposition, but many of the more simple types can be tested in this manner. When a fault is proving to be difficult to locate, testing the semiconductors, preferably with them completely removed from the circuit board, is always a good idea. If one or more of the semiconductors proves to be faulty, then replacing the faulty component or components will probably cure the problem (but note the warning given previously). If the semiconductors prove to be fully serviceable, then you know that the problem is in the passive components or the soldering, and you can go on to check these.

As I have pointed out many times before, and will no doubt explain many more times in the future, if a newly constructed project fails to work, probably more than nine times out of ten it is due to a bad joint, a short circuit due to a solder splash, or something of this nature. With a newly constructed project where the semiconductors prove to be functioning correctly, the board itself is probably the part of the unit to concentrate on next. With a project that has worked correctly but has become faulty, the passive components would represent the most likely cause of the problem.

For the checks described here the particular breadboard used is not too important. The test circuits are so simple that virtually any breadboard should suffice, but it obviously needs to be a reasonably modern type capable of taking integrated circuits with 0.1 inch pin spacing (or one fitted with a carrier for standard d.i.l. integrated circuits).

Operational amplifiers represent one of the most simple types of integrated circuit as far as testing is concerned. They are easily tested by using them as voltage comparators, as in the simple test circuit of Figure 1.10. An operational amplifier is a differential amplifier, which simply means that it amplifies the voltage difference across its inputs. If the non-inverting (+) input is at a higher voltage than the inverting (−) input, the output goes positive. If the relative input voltages are reversed, the output goes positive. In practice the d.c. voltage gain of an operational amplifier that is used open loop (i.e. without any negative feedback) is very high, being typically about 200,000 times. Therefore, only a minute voltage difference is needed across the inputs in order to send the output fully positive or negative.

In the test circuit of Figure 1.10 a fixed potential of about half the supply voltage is fed to the inverting input of the test device by the potential divider circuit formed by R1 and R2. VR1 permits a variable voltage to be fed to the non-inverting input. If VR1 is initially set for minimum voltage at its wiper, and then steadily advanced, the output voltage from the circuit should initially be quite low, but should suddenly jump to almost the full supply voltage with VR1 at roughly the middle of its adjustment range. Due to the very high open loop gain of an operational amplifier, it should be virtually impossible to set VR1 to give an intermediate output voltage. In fact with many operational amplifiers it may well prove

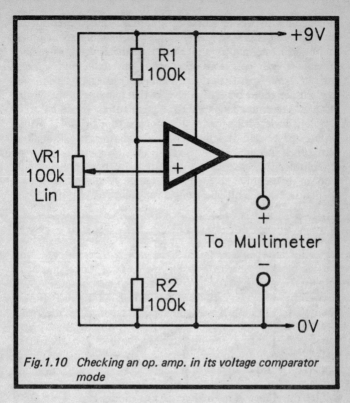

Fig.1.10   Checking an op. amp. in its voltage comparator mode

to be totally impossible to obtain an intermediate output voltage.

Do not expect the maximum and minimum output voltages from the operational amplifier to be equal to the positive and negative supply potentials. With most operational amplifiers (including the standard µA741C and most of its bipolar and f.e.t. equivalents) the maximum output voltage falls about 1 volt or so short of the positive supply potential. The minimum output voltage is often more than 2 volts, but with some MOS and bipolar types (such as the CA3130E, CA3140E, LM358, and LM324) the minimum output voltage can go to within a few millivolts of the negative supply voltage. Modern operational amplifiers almost invariably have good immunity to latch-up. This is where the output voltage goes to the wrong level because the differential input voltage is excessive, or one or both inputs are taken outside their normal operating voltage range. This latch-up could result in the output going high with VR1 set for around minimum voltage, or low when it is set for about maximum voltage (i.e. jumping to the wrong state at the extremes of VR1's adjustment range). Few non-obsolete devices suffer from this problem though, and it would be as well to be suspicious of any modern device that does have this trait.

Another very simple but useful test for operational amplifiers is to try them as voltage followers, as in the test circuit of Figure 1.11. With 100% negative feedback from the output

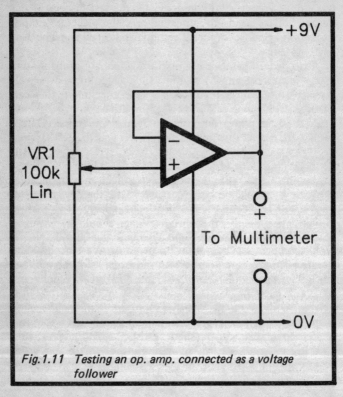

Fig. 1.11   Testing an op. amp. connected as a voltage follower

to the inverting input of the amplifier, it has unity voltage gain from the non-inverting input to the output. VR1 can be used to set any input voltage between 0 volts and 9 volts, and in theory the output voltage measured on the multimeter should be exactly the same as the input voltage. In practice the output voltage limitations of the operational amplifier must be taken into account. As pointed out previously, for most devices this means that the minimum output potential will be about 2 volts, and the maximum will be around 1 to 1.5 volts less than the positive supply voltage. With appropriate types, the minimum output voltage will be insignificantly more than 0 volts.

Adjustment of VR1 should give a smooth variation between the output voltage limits imposed by the test device. If the output voltage tends to jump all over the place, or simply stays fully positive or negative, this indicates that the test device is faulty.

Apart from operational amplifiers, there are probably not many linear integrated circuits which lend themselves well to simple test setups of this type. It is a technique that can be used with some audio power amplifiers though. Some modern audio power amplifier integrated circuits are effectively high power operational amplifiers, and the test circuits of Figures 1.10 and 1.11 should work perfectly well with these. With a device such as the LM380N, which has built-in bias components, this method of testing is not applicable. However, it would be quite feasible to fit the device onto a breadboard and connect it to a 9 volt supply. If its biasing is working correctly, the output voltage should be within a few percent of half the supply voltage.

Digital I.C.s

Simple static testing circuits are easily applied to many types of digital integrated circuit, including gates, decoders, multiplexer, etc. On the other hand, there are some logic devices that are essentially dynamic in their function, and which can not be fully tested by taking d.c. voltage checks. The techniques described here can be used to good effect with most of the digital integrated circuits used in home constructor designs though.

The basic action of many digital integrated circuits is to produce a certain output state, or set of output states, for a given set of input logic levels. Gates, inverters and decoders, for example, fall into this category. The usual way of showing the function of these more simple logic devices is by way of a "truth table". In its most basic form this just consists of a list of input states, with the output state or states being shown for each set of input conditions. For instance, this is the truth table for a three input AND gate.

INPUT 1	INPUT 2	INPUT 3	OUTPUT
LOW	LOW	LOW	LOW
LOW	LOW	HIGH	LOW
LOW	HIGH	LOW	LOW
LOW	HIGH	HIGH	LOW
HIGH	LOW	LOW	LOW
HIGH	LOW	HIGH	LOW
HIGH	HIGH	LOW	LOW
HIGH	HIGH	HIGH	HIGH

Integrated circuits of this type are easily tested with the aid of a breadboard, a power source, a multimeter, and a few link wires. First wire the supply pins of the chip to a suitable power source. For most logic devices this means a 5 volt supply, and virtually all modern bench power supplies can provide a 5 volt output. Improvising a temporary power source using batteries is not easy as 1.5 volt cells can obviously not provide 5 volts. Three cells gives about 4.5 volts, or four cells gives around 6 volts. When testing logic integrated circuits you need to bear in mind that many of them are only guaranteed to operate with a supply voltage that is within a few percent of the specified supply potential. The acceptable voltage range depends on the logic family from which the test device is taken. Note that the supply voltage range is not the same for all the logic families under the general TTL heading ("LS", "HC", "HCT", etc.). Some of the CMOS TTL devices have relatively wide supply voltage ranges, and should operate properly with a 3 volt, 4.5 volt, or 6 volt battery supply.

With many logic families there is only a 5% tolerance on the supply voltage (i.e. it should be between 4.75 and 5.25

volts). In practice a 4.5 volt or 6 volt supply is likely to be satisfactory for static tests, but it is obviously better if the supply voltage is within the chip manufacturer's recommended operating range. The results of tests are then conclusive. A simple way of providing an accurate 5 volt supply is to use a 9 volt battery plus a 5 volt monolithic voltage regulator, as in the circuit of Figure 1.12. The additional components should be easily accommodated on the breadboard.

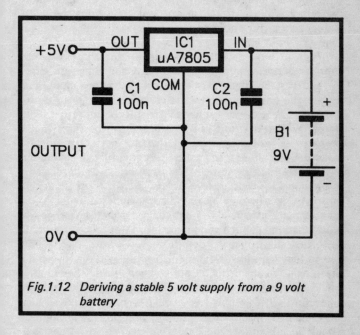

Fig.1.12   Deriving a stable 5 volt supply from a 9 volt battery

Testing ordinary CMOS logic circuits is less problematic. The operating voltage range of old devices is about 3 to 15 volts, and with modern types the acceptable supply voltage range is 3 to 18 volts. A 3, 4.5, 6, or 9 volt battery supply is adequate for testing purposes. Some TTL devices have quite high supply currents even under static operating conditions, but the quiescent current consumption of most CMOS devices, including many of the more complex ones, is negligible. A small (PP3 size) 9 volt battery is therefore perfectly suitable as the power source.

Having connected the supply, the next step is to use the link wires to set up the first set of input states. Simply connect inputs to the positive supply rail if they must be taken high, or to the negative supply if they must be set to the low state. The multimeter is then used to measure the output voltage or voltages, to ensure that they are correct. Then the link wires are adjusted to set up the next set of input states, the output voltage should be checked again using the multimeter, and so on until the output voltage has been checked for every set of input states.

This can be rather time-consuming, especially when you consider that each integrated circuit may contain several gates. In fact it is the single gate chips with numerous inputs that require the longest test procedures. An eight input gate for instance, has some two hundred and fifty-six different input states. With devices of this type it is probably best to rationalise the test procedure to a considerable degree in order to make the task more manageable. Suppose that an eight input NAND gate must be tested. The basic action of this device is to provide a low output level unless all eight of its inputs are high. Obviously only testing all two hundred and fifty-six input conditions would give definite proof that the device was fully functioning, but a good rationalised test procedure would be to first check that the output was low with all eight inputs tied to the high state. Next input 1 would be taken low, and a check made to see if the output had gone low. Then input 1 would be returned to the high state, and input 2 would be taken low. The output level would then be checked again. Next input 2 would be returned to the high state, input 3 would be taken low, the output voltage would be checked, and this procedure would be continued until all the inputs had been tested in the low state. If each input was able to exercise control over the output, then it would be highly unlikely that the device was faulty. This is the rationalised truth table for an eight input NAND gate.

| INPUTS | | | | | | | | OUTPUT |
1	2	3	4	5	6	7	8	
H	H	H	H	H	H	H	H	L
L	H	H	H	H	H	H	H	H
H	L	H	H	H	H	H	H	H
H	H	L	H	H	H	H	H	H
H	H	H	L	H	H	H	H	H
H	H	H	H	L	H	H	H	H
H	H	H	H	H	L	H	H	H
H	H	H	H	H	H	L	H	H
H	H	H	H	H	H	H	L	H

Logic Voltages

In order to interpret the results of this form of testing you
need to know the valid voltage ranges for the logic 0 and logic
1 levels. When testing the CMOS 4000 range of integrated
circuits there is no great difficulty here. Logic 0 ("low")
should give a voltage reading that is so low it will probably
fail to register on the meter, while logic 1 ("high") should
give a reading that is virtually equal to the positive supply
potential. This is due to the use of complimentary output
transistors, which gives the effective output circuit of Figure
1.13(a) when an output is high, and that of Figure 1.13(b)
when it is low. The low value resistor is the resistance of the
transistor that is switched on, while the very high value
resistor is the resistance of the transistor that is switched off.
The very high "on" to "off" resistance ratio of the output
transistors ensures that the unloaded peak-to-peak output
voltage is not significantly less than the supply voltage.

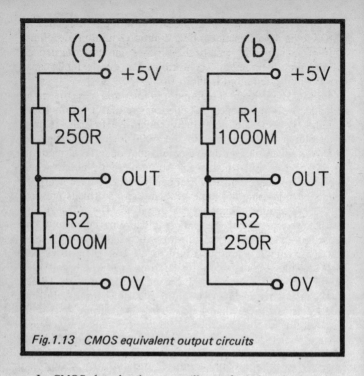

Fig.1.13 CMOS equivalent output circuits

In CMOS data books you will not find that the high and low logic levels are stated as being within a few millivolts of their respective supply voltages. Logic 0 is usually given as something like 0 to 30% of the supply potential, with logic 1 at anywhere between 70 and 100% of the supply voltage. These are voltage ranges to which the inputs of a CMOS device are guaranteed to respond properly. With the outputs of CMOS devices switching almost fully between the two supply levels, this may all seem to be of academic importance. However, you must remember that in normal use CMOS outputs may be switching between the two logic levels at a high frequency, and they may then fail to reach the same voltage levels that are achieved in static tests. Perhaps of more relevance in the current context, CMOS outputs are sometimes loaded more heavily than the very light loading provided by a multimeter or several CMOS inputs. The input resistance to CMOS logic devices incidentally, is about a million megohms. This gives what for practical purposes can be regarded as infinite fanout under d.c. conditions, but due to input capacity the dynamic fanout is about fifty.

If a CMOS logic integrated circuit produces the right unloaded output voltages, the chances are that it is fully functioning. Results are not totally conclusive though. I have encountered CMOS devices in the 4000 logic family that do not work when plugged into a circuit that operates at medium to high speeds, but which seems to be perfectly alright when subjected to static and low frequency tests. I have heard of others encountering the same problem, and so this is presumably a reasonably common type of fault. The cause of the problem seems to be that an overload on the output has caused an excessive output current which has damaged one of the complementary output transistors. This then provides a high resistance load for the other transistor which acts as a simple common source switch having a resistive load. Under static tests this might give quite plausible results, but at frequencies of more than a few hertz the output stage fails to work due to the low "on" output current and stray capacitance slowing down the switching time to inadequate level.

A safer method of making static tests on CMOS logic integrated circuits is to connect the multimeter to a potential divider connected across the supply rails, and to then connect this to each of the test points in turn via a link-wire, as in Figure 1.14. The potential divider tries to pull the test point to about half the supply voltage, but the output under test tries to pull the test point high or low. The output, if it is functioning correctly, will largely win the battle, as its output transistors can provide a resistance that is significantly lower than the value used in the potential divider. The output voltages will fall significantly short of either supply voltage, but will be well within the acceptable ranges of 0 to 30% and 70 to 100% of the supply voltage. If one of the output transistors is damaged, then one of the logic levels will be achieved properly, but with the output set to the other logic state the output voltage will be about half the supply voltage.

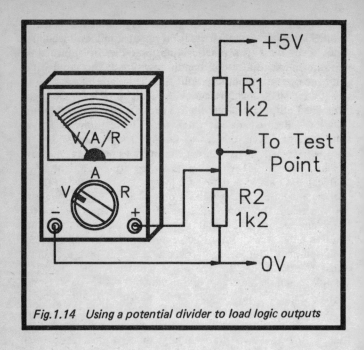

Fig.1.14   Using a potential divider to load logic outputs

TTL Outputs

The acceptable output voltage range for TTL devices varies slightly from one type to another. However, in general, and for types which operate from a 5 volt supply, a logic 0 level is anything from 0 to 0.8 volts, and a high level is anything from 2 to 5 volts. This gives a relatively narrow range of illegal voltages, but in practice an unloaded TTL output will be little more than 0 volts when it is low, and around 4 volts when it is high. Faults in the output stages of TTL devices, in my experience anyway, seem to be more rare than those in CMOS types. It would probably still be a good idea to use the method of loading described previously when testing TTL integrated circuits though.

If you are testing TTL devices that can operate on a supply potential of other than 5 volts, and you are having to use a supply voltage of other than 5 volts, then the acceptable voltage levels for each logic level must be adjusted proportionately in order to match the change in supply voltage. You could consult the data sheet/book for the device concerned if you want more accurate information about the valid voltage ranges for various supply voltages. However, in practice the outputs will probably go to what are clearly acceptable voltages or completely invalid potentials, making any highly accurate voltage tests unnecessary.

Tristate Outputs

There is a slight complication when testing many logic integrated circuits in that they have "tristate" outputs, or "three state" outputs as they are also known. Apart from the usual high and low levels, these have an "off" state. In this state the output has a very high output impedance, and it goes to a logic level determined by some other device. This other device is usually the output of another logic element, an input, or a pull-up/pull-down resistor.

Testing a tristate device should not present any real difficulties, and it is again just a matter of including the potential divider in the test circuit. High and low logic levels will produce the appropriate voltage levels, while the "off" state should result in the output being taken to around half the supply voltage by the potential divider circuit.

Decoders Etc.

Obviously many logic integrated circuits are not simple gates and inverters, and provide more complex tasks. Despite this, many logic devices can be tested using simple static voltage checks. As an example, take the popular 74LS138 three to eight line decoder integrated circuit. This has the pinout arrangement illustrated in Figure 1.15.

The basic function of this device is to activate one of the outputs ("0" to "7"), with the activated output being selected by the binary number fed to the three main inputs ("A" to "C"). Input "A" is the least significant bit – input "C" is the most significant bit. "000" on these inputs would activate output "0", 001 activates output "1", 010 activates output "2", and so on through to 111 activating output "7". The

29

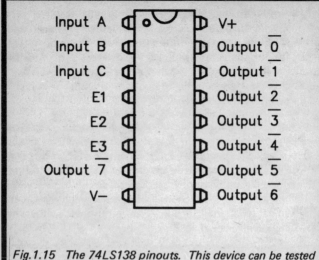

Fig.1.15 The 74LS138 pinouts. This device can be tested
in much the same way as logic gates

outputs are all active low types, so the activated output is
low while all the others are in the high state.

Testing a device of this type does not pose any real problems, and the same basic techniques that are used with gates
would seem to be equally applicable to a device of this type.
It is just a matter of wiring the inputs, in turn, to each of the
eight different sets of input states. For each set of input
conditions the outputs must be checked to ensure that the
right one, and only the right one, is in the low state.

There is an added complication in that the 74LS138 has
three enable inputs; two negative ones (pins 4 and 5) and one
positive type (pin 6). When carrying out the test procedure
described above it would be necessary for each of these to be
taken to their active state. If the initial test procedure gave
positive results, it would then be necessary to test the enable
inputs. This is just a matter of measuring the output voltage

30

from the activated output, using the potential divider loading described previously. In turn, the three enable inputs are then taken to their non-active states, which in each case should result in the output voltage going to about half the supply voltage (i.e. the output should go to the "off" state).

Static Dynamic Testing

Using a multimeter it is obviously not possible to undertake high speed dynamic tests on logic integrated circuits. On the other hand, it is quite possible to slow down the operating speed of a test circuit to the point where a multimeter can be used to check that outputs are at the correct logic levels. This is a sort of cross between true dynamic and true static testing. The multimeter is measuring static voltages, but they need only be maintained for a second or two, after which the circuit is clocked on to the next phase by an input pulse so that the next voltage check can be made.

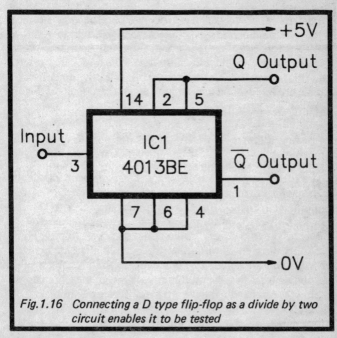

Fig.1.16 Connecting a D type flip-flop as a divide by two circuit enables it to be tested

31

As a simple example of how this type of testing can be undertaken, consider the circuit of Figure 1.16. This has one half of the 4013BE dual D type flip/flop connected as a divide by two circuit. In common with most flip/flops (and several other types of logic circuit elements) this one has two outputs. These are the "Q" and "not Q" outputs (the latter having the "not" bar over the Q). They differ in that the Q input is active high, whereas the not Q output is active low. On successive input pulses the Q input should be toggled from one logic level to the other, and the not Q input should always be at the opposite state.

Testing this circuit requires a low frequency input signal at about one pulse every two to five seconds. Most logic pulsers can provide a signal of this type or a simple clock oscillator can be breadboarded together with the rest of the circuit. A suitable circuit based on the ever useful 555 timer integrated circuit is provided in Figure 1.17. Another alternative, and quite a good one, is to use a push button switch to permit input pulses to be generated manually. The only problem with this method is that contact bounce tends to result in push button switches generating numerous spurious output pulses. These would obviously result in misleading results, and they must be suppressed. This is easily done using a simple active debouncing circuit, as in the circuit of Figure 1.18.

Monitoring the two outputs of a flip/flop presents a slight problem. One solution is to use a low enough clock frequency to permit the multimeter to be used to measure both voltages, in turn, between clock pulses. If you have two multimeters, and a lot of people these days have both analogue and digital instruments, then there is obviously no difficulty. Use one multimeter to check the Q output, and the other to test the not Q output. Another method is to measure the voltage across the two outputs. Assuming that a 5 volt supply is used, the differential output voltage should alternate between +5 volts and −5 volts. Obviously this method is only possible if you are using a digital multimeter, or one of the few analogue types that can handle input voltages of either polarity.

To test the divide by two flip/flop circuit, check that each input pulse results in both outputs changing state. Pin 4 is the

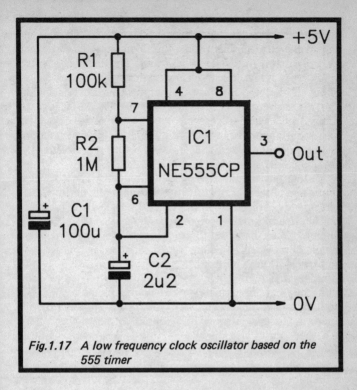

*Fig.1.17 A low frequency clock oscillator based on the
555 timer*

reset input, and if this is taken high it should result in the Q
output going low and the not Q output going high. The
divide by two action will be inhibited while the reset input
is high. If the reset input is returned to the low state, and the
set input (pin 6) is taken high, the Q output should be forced
high, the not Q output should be forced low, and the divide
by two action should again be inhibited.

These methods of testing can be applied to other logic
integrated circuits, including some that, on the face of it,
represent what might reasonably be termed a testing time.
A 74LS273 8-bit D type flip/flop is a good example of an
integrated circuit which falls into this category. This is quite
a complex device which has the pinout configuration shown
in Figure 1.19. Probably the most common application of this

33

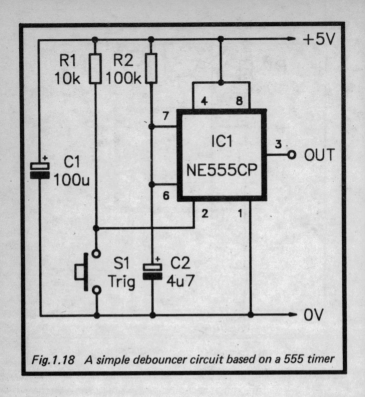

Fig.1.18 A simple debouncer circuit based on a 555 timer

device is as an eight bit data latch. When used in this role the eight data inputs ("D0" to "D7") are fed from something like the data bus of a microprocessor. A negative pulse from the address decoder or other control logic circuit is applied to the "CP" (clock pulse) input in order to latch the bit pattern on the eight inputs onto the eight outputs ("Q0" to "Q7"). The MR input is the master reset input, and taking this low sets all the outputs low and inhibits the device.

The obvious first test on this device is to take the master reset terminal low, and to check that this sets all the outputs low. Then set up a bit pattern on the inputs by (say) wiring D0 to D3 low, and D4 to D7 high. Applying a pulse to the clock pulse input should result in this bit pattern being transferred to the outputs. If the device is providing the correct

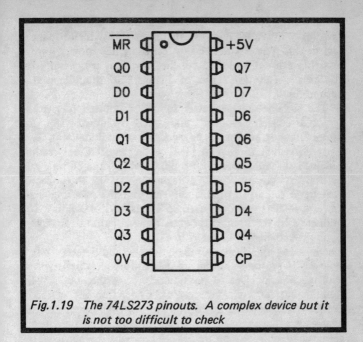

Fig.1.19   The 74LS273 pinouts. A complex device but it is not too difficult to check

latching action, changing the bit pattern at the inputs should have no effect on the bit pattern on the outputs.

With a little ingenuity it should be possible to test virtually any logic integrated circuit, including such things as multi-bit latches, magnitude comparators, and multiplexer. You need to be familiar with the functions of the devices you are trying to test though, and as with most testing, the better your technical knowledge the greater your chances of carrying out the task successfully.

Component Analysis

In BP239 a method of using a multimeter plus a few other components as a transistor current gain meter was described. This basic concept can be extended to permit virtually any static parameter of a transistor to be checked, and it can also be used with other components. Suppose that you wish to test the gain of a transistor at specific collector voltage and current levels, because your data on the device only gives a gain range at these figures. Also, you may wish to make a test of this type if you need to test some high power transistors that can not be tested conclusively using many transistor checkers. The test setup of Figure 1.20 should give the desired result.

The variable voltage power supply is adjusted to give the required collector voltage, and VR1 is adjusted for the required collector current, as registered on multimeter 2. This current reading is then divided by the base current reading obtained on multimeter 1 in order to obtain the current gain of the test transistor. As an example, suppose the collector current is set at 100 milliamps and that the measured base current is 850 microamps (0.85 milliamps). Dividing 100 milliamps by 0.85 milliamps gives the d.c. current gain figure of about 118 (100/0.85 = 117.64).

Obviously this test setup calls for two multimeters, but if you only have one multimeter it is still usable. Start with a shorting link in place of multimeter 1, and then adjust VR1 for the correct collector current. Then use the meter in position one, and use a shorting link for multimeter 2. This enables the base current to be measured so that the current gain calculation can be made. If you wish to be pedantic, you can use resistors instead of shorting links in order to mimic the resistance of the multimeter. You can also adjust the supply voltage slightly higher in order to compensate for the voltage drop through multimeter 2, and thus give exactly the required collector voltage. In practice this sort of thing is probably not worthwhile, and is unlikely to give much improvement in the accuracy of results.

This sort of improvised setup can be used to test the more obscure aspects of semiconductors. Suppose you have a thyristor which is not behaving as expected, but passes the resistance checks described previously, and seems alright when subjected to a simple trigger test (as described on page 60 of BP239). One possibility would be that the hold-on characteristic of the device is not within the specified limits. Remember that a thyristor, unlike a transistor, remains switched on even if the input current is removed. It can only be switched off by reducing the current flow between the

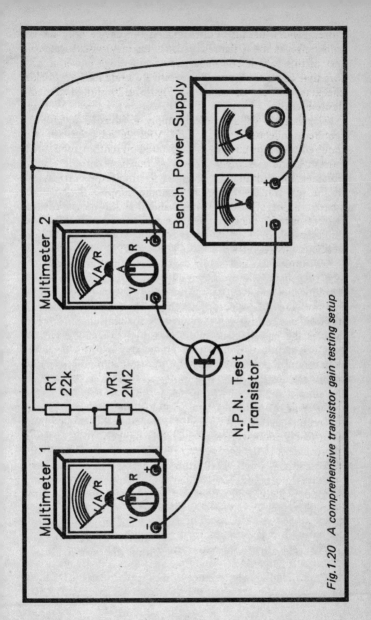

Fig. 1.20 A comprehensive transistor gain testing setup

anode and cathode terminals below a certain threshold level. This is called the "hold-on" or "holding" current, or is usually termed "Ihm" in thyristor data sheets and books.

The holding current could be checked using the simple test circuit of Figure 1.21. VR1 is initially set at minimum resistance so that a fairly high current flow is produced when the test device is triggered. To trigger the thyristor it is merely necessary to momentarily operate push button switch PB1. In fact you do not need to have a push button switch here — briefly fitting a shorting wire in this part of the circuit will trigger the thyristor. Once it has been triggered, the multimeter should register the anode current, and this current should be maintained when the trigger current to the gate is removed. By adjusting VR1 it is possible to vary the anode current, and it is a matter of slowly adjusting this control for a reducing anode current while carefully monitoring results on the multimeter. At some stage the current reading will suddenly drop to zero. The holding current is the reading that was obtained just before the meter indicated zero current flow.

If the holding current is very low, the cut off might not be obtained even with VR1 adjusted for maximum resistance. Adding another fixed value resistor in series with VR1 will permit lower currents to be accommodated by the test circuit. Alternatively, you might simply decide to temporarily short circuit the anode and cathode terminals of the thyristor to reduce the anode current to zero, to check that the device does not have a tendency to stick in the "on" state.

Another important thyristor parameter is the maximum gate trigger current ("Ig" in the data books). Note that this figure is not the maximum permissible gate current, but the maximum input current that will be needed in order to trigger the device. With many modern thyristors this figure is only a fraction of a milliamp, whereas it is typically about 20 to 30 milliamps with most of the older types. Using a type that has a high trigger current could obviously prevent the circuit from operating if it is designed for a modern high sensitivity type.

The gate trigger current can be measured using the test circuit of Figure 1.22. This time start with VR1 at maximum resistance, and slowly advance it until l.e.d. indicator D1 lights up (which indicates that the thyristor has triggered). The

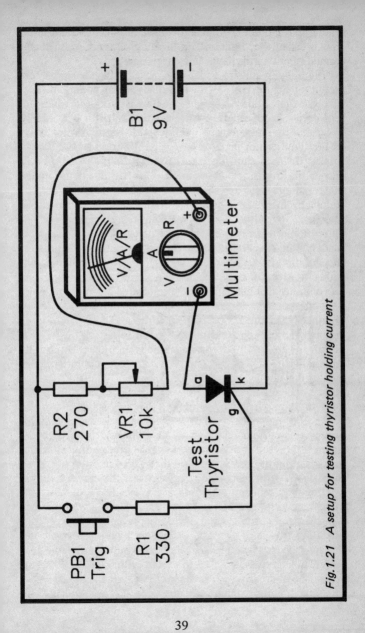

Fig. 1.21 A setup for testing thyristor holding current

39

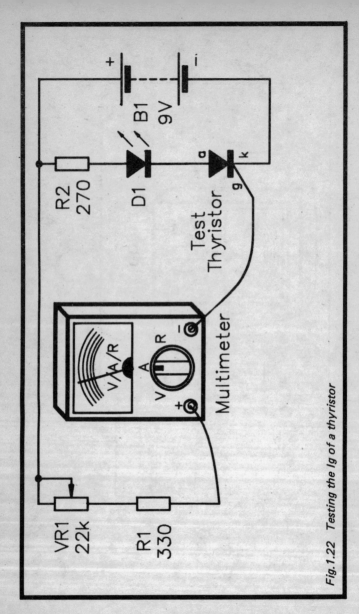

Fig. 1.22 Testing the Ig of a thyristor

reading on the multimeter then indicates the gate trigger current at which the device is activated.

There are plenty of pieces of test gear for testing components such as diodes, transistors, resistors, and capacitors, but you can not expect to have specialist test equipment to cover all component testing. The range and diversity of modern electronic components is such that even if a full range of component testing equipment could be purchased or home constructed, so many pieces of equipment would be needed that it would not be a practical proposition to do so. In practice you are unlikely to find test equipment to meet all your component testing requirements anyway. Simple breadboard test circuits utilizing one or two multimeters represent a versatile and inexpensive solution to the problem. If you understand the function of a component and its d.c. characteristics, then it will almost certainly be possible to test it using a simple improvised test circuit.

L.E.D.s and L.C.D.s

The testing of light emitting diodes was covered in BP239. It is basically just a matter of switching the multimeter to a suitable resistance range and connecting it to the l.e.d. with the appropriate polarity. If the l.e.d. is functioning correctly it should light up. This method of testing should work equally well with seven segment displays and bargraph types. The segments of a seven segment display are given identifying letters from "A" to "G", and the decimal point is usually just abbreviated to "DP". Figure 1.23 shows the standard arrangement of the segments in one of these displays.

When testing a common cathode type, connect the positive test prod to the cathode terminal, and then touch the negative test prod onto each of the other terminals in turn to see if the appropriate segments light up. For a common anode display, connect the negative test prod to the anode, and the positive test prod to each of the cathodes. This assumes you are using an analogue multimeter — the test prods must be connected the other way round if you use a digital type.

Infra-red l.e.d.s, as used in remote control systems etc., pose a slight problem. All the components of this type I have encountered fail to produce any visible light output at all.

41

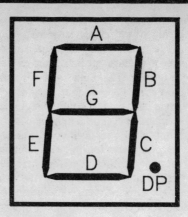

Fig.1.23 *The segment layout for a seven segment display.*
These are easily checked using the resistance
range of a multimeter.

However, simply testing that an infra-red l.e.d. provides a diode action should give a good indication of whether or not the component is functioning properly. If it does not provide a diode action, then it is certainly faulty. If it does, then it is possible but highly unlikely that it is faulty.

As a more comprehensive test you could try the simple test circuit of Figure 1.24. This uses a 9 volt battery and current limiting resistor R1 to bias the infra-red diode into conduction. Its infra-red output is directed at photocell PCC1, which is the ever popular ORP12 cadmium sulphide cell, but virtually any other cadmium sulphide photo-resistor should be suitable. The resistance of PCC1 is measured using the multimeter. If the battery is disconnected from the infra-red l.e.d. its output will be cut off, the light level reaching PCC1 will decrease, and a higher reading should be shown on the multimeter. It is not necessary for this test to be carried out in near or total darkness, but you should try to keep the photocell shielded from any strong sources of light. The lower the ambient light level

42

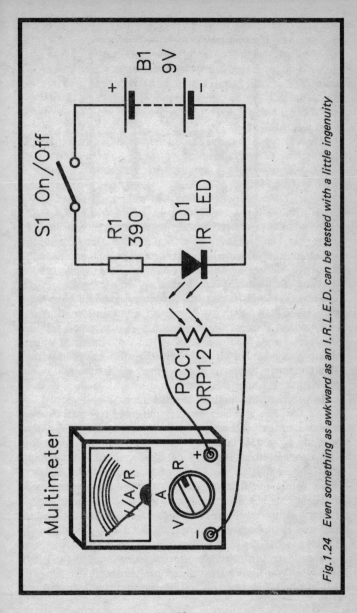

Fig. 1.24 Even something as awkward as an I.R.L.E.D. can be tested with a little ingenuity

43

reaching PCC1, the more pronounced the change in PCC1's resistance should become.

Although cadmium sulphide photo-resistors are often thought of as only visible light detectors, they offer good sensitivity at the light wavelengths produced by infra-red light emitting diodes. In common with many photo devices, most cadmium sulphide photocells offer peak sensitivity to this part of the spectrum.

Liquid crystal displays (l.c.d.s) represent a difficult type of component to test. In normal use the common terminal is connected to earth or a pseudo-earth, and the other terminals are fed with a low frequency a.c. drive signal if their respective segments must be switched on. In some cases the display is driven from anti-phase outputs providing a varying d.c. signal, giving what is effectively an a.c. signal across any display segment that is activated. This second method is popular for low voltage battery powered equipment as it enables about double the drive voltage to be achieved for a given supply voltage.

Although liquid crystal displays are driven from a.c. signal sources, they will in fact operate properly if fed with a d.c. signal of either polarity. If you set a multimeter to a resistance range, connect one test prod to the common terminal (the metal plate at the rear of most l.c.d.s provides an easy connection point), and then apply the other test prod to each of the segment terminals in turn, good segments should switch on when their terminal is connected.

In practice this method of testing has to be regarded as a little risky. Firstly, you should not use a high resistance range where the test voltage could be excessive for the display. Secondly, the reason liquid crystal displays are driven with a.c. signals is that they are damaged by d.c. signals. Quite small d.c. signals over a period of time can lead to failure of these components, and with large d.c. signals they can be damaged in a matter of minutes. Provided you only apply a d.c. signal to each segment for a second or so, there is probably no danger of significantly shortening the life of the display. I have used this method of testing in the past, and have not noticed any long term problems with the displays. However, you have been warned of the danger, and it is up to you whether or not you use this method of testing.

Finally

When testing any components you need to take great care not to add to any faults already present in equipment. You need to be particularly careful with MOS integrated circuits. A lot of the warnings about handling precautions for these devices are a bit over the top, and many of the recommendations are certainly not practical propositions for amateur users. However, you should avoid having any obvious sources of high static voltages near these components, and handle them no more than is reasonably necessary. Avoid using test techniques that could apply excessive voltages to the inputs of test components. If the general techniques described in this chapter are applied sensibly, a wide range of devices can be thoroughly and safely tested.

Chapter 2

EXTENDING YOUR MULTIMETER

A multimeter, even one having a fairly basic specification, is undoubtedly a very versatile piece of test equipment. However, with the addition of some simple pieces of electronics it is surprising how much more can be brought within the repertoire of a multimeter. In this chapter several simple add-on circuits are described, including such things as an active r.f. probe, high input impedance boosters, and memory units. These should enable your multimeter to reach the parts that other multimeters can not reach!

R.F. Voltages

The problems of r.f. voltage measurement were discussed in BP239. In brief, the main problem is that of most multimeters having a.c. voltage ranges that only cover the audio frequency range. In fact a few analogue multimeters do cover frequencies well into r.f. spectrum, and one analogue instrument I had seemed quite happy measuring signals at about 50MHz! This is the exception rather than the rule though, and an upper frequency response that falls away rapidly above about 20kHz would seem to be more normal these days. The situation is worse with digital multimeters, where it is unusual to have a.c. ranges that have good accuracy beyond a few hundred hertz.

A second problem is that of the input capacitance. This tends to give strong detuning or loading if a simple a.c. voltmeter circuit is used to measure medium or high impedance r.f. signal sources. The severity of the problem depends very much on the circuit involved. Many modern digital circuits use a crystal controlled clock oscillator, and with the current low cost of crystals even some quite simple digital devices now sport a crystal controlled clock circuit. The configuration shown in Figure 2.1 is a popular one, and on the face of it there is not likely to be any real difficulty if it is checked with a simple a.c. voltmeter circuit to see if there is any output from the circuit. The output would seem to be at a reasonably low impedance.

47

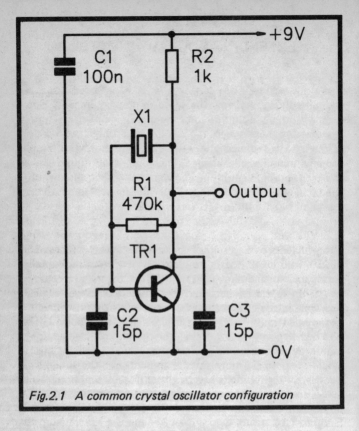

Fig.2.1 A common crystal oscillator configuration

In practice it is quite possible that checking the output from the collector of TR1 with such an instrument would cause the oscillator to cease operating. Capacitors C2 and C3 effectively form a capacitive tapping on the tuned circuit, which in this case is crystal X1. These two capacitors do not need to be very accurately matched in order to obtain the desired circuit action with a phase inversion through the crystal so that positive feedback is obtained. However, a gross mis-match here and too little feedback to sustain oscillation will result. With this type of circuit the two capacitors are usually at values of around 10p to 47p, and the input capacitance of a simple a.c. voltmeter, especially if it does not use a probe type detector, could effectively boost the value of C2 by a few hundred percent.

The accepted way of obtaining a high input impedance at high frequencies with minimal shunt capacitance is to use an active probe. In other words, a probe unit that contains a buffer amplifier plus the rectifier and smoothing circuit. The output of the circuit is at d.c., and any stray capacitance in the output cable (which could be quite considerable) is of no real consequence. It is swamped by the very much higher value smoothing capacitance connected across the output of the rectifier and smoothing circuit. The lack of any cable at the input of a probe helps to keep the input capacitance to a minimum, and with an active type the isolation between the input and the rectifier and smoothing circuit helps to further minimise the input capacitance. Obviously the buffer amplifier will have a certain amount of input capacitance, but this need be no more than about 10p or so. While any input capacitance is undesirable, about 10p is the minimum that can be readily achieved in practice, and is low enough to give excellent results in virtually all circumstances.

The Circuit
Figure 2.2 shows the circuit diagram for a simple but useful active r.f. probe. I built this for use with a 20k/volt analogue multimeter, but it should be usable with any multimeter, from low sensitivity analogue types through to digital and high impedance analogue instruments. The buffer amplifier is based on TR1, which is a Jfet device used in the common drain (or source follower) mode. This gives a little less than unity voltage gain, which is all we require in this application. The advantage of a source follower stage is that it gives a high input resistance and low input capacitance. The input resistance is only fractionally less than the value of gate bias resistor R1, which is 10 megohms in this circuit. With the source follower mode there is no Miller Effect to multiply the basic input capacitance of the transistor, and this gives an input capacitance of only about 10p.

The rectifier stage is a conventional twin diode half wave type, using germanium diodes to minimise the losses through

49

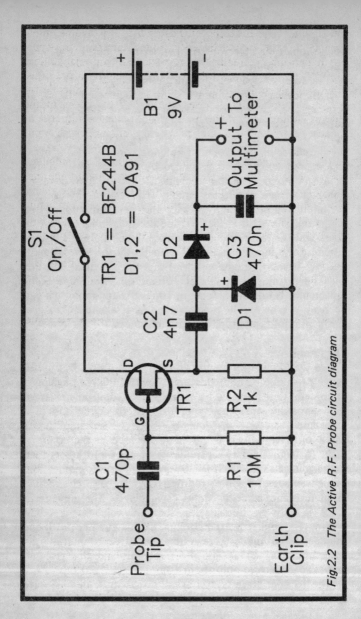

Fig.2.2 The Active R.F. Probe circuit diagram

50

the circuit. C3 is the smoothing capacitor. It would be unreasonable to expect good linearity from a circuit of this type, but it performs better in this respect than you might think. The d.c. output voltage is approximately equal to the r.m.s. input voltage, and although the unit may not be suitable for precise measurements, it gives you a very good idea of the voltage level present at the input. The frequency response of the unit is quite good, and it should work well with input frequencies anywhere in the range 100kHz to 50MHz.

It is important to keep in mind that the unit is not intended for use with anything other than low voltage circuits, and that it will not function properly with input levels of more than a few volts peak-to-peak. Obviously these days most radio frequency circuits are low voltage semiconductor types, and relatively few electronics hobbyists have the need to test high voltage valve or semiconductor circuits which have high voltage supplies. If you should use the unit with circuits of this type there is a definite risk of damaging the semiconductors in the probe, especially TR1.

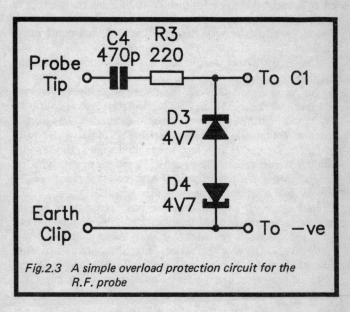

Fig.2.3 A simple overload protection circuit for the
R.F. probe

51

This risk can be minimised by adding the protection circuit of Figure 2.3. This consists of a series resistor plus zener diodes D1 and D2 to clip the input signal at approximately plus and minus 5.4 volts. Regardless of the input signal's polarity, one diode will act as a standard zener while the other will operate as a forward biased silicon diode. They provide approximate clipping levels of 4.7 and 0.7 volts respectively, giving a combined clipping level of plus and minus 5.4 volts.

I would not recommend fitting this protection circuit unless you are likely to use the unit on circuits that could provide dangerously high input voltages. The diodes are used in a series arrangement rather than a parallel one so as to minimise their capacitance, but they still give a substantial boost to the probe's input capacitance. This, together with input resistor R1, form a lowpass filter. This significantly impairs the high frequency performance of the circuit.

As always, unless you are completely sure you know what you are doing, you should not test any circuits which contain high voltages. Do not use a unit of this type on mains powered equipment that does not include an isolating transformer to give a chassis that is properly isolated from the mains supply. To do so would be very dangerous indeed, and could prove fatal.

The circuit is very simple, and it is easily constructed using stripboard or a custom printed circuit board. Try to keep the layout compact so that the unit can be made as small as possible. The layout is not particularly critical, with no likelihood of the circuit breaking into oscillation. Designing a compact component layout is therefore quite straightforward. Note that D1 and D2 are germanium diodes, and not the more familiar silicon variety. The practical importance of this is that they are more easily damaged by heat, and due care needs to be exercised when soldering them into circuit.

Mechanically, construction of any probe-type project requires a certain amount of ingenuity. You may be able to obtain a probe type case that will accommodate all the components including the battery, but it is quite possible that you will have to improvise using a small plastic case. Several cases of this type are available quite cheaply. A suggested form for the unit is shown in Figure 2.4. To keep the unit

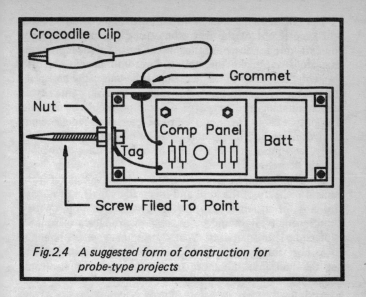

Fig.2.4 A suggested form of construction for probe-type projects

reasonably small and light the battery must be a low capacity type, such as one of the PP3 size batteries that are readily available. A low capacity battery is quite adequate as the current consumption of the circuit is only a few milliamps, and it is not necessary to use one of the expensive "high power" types.

The connection to the earth rail is made via an insulated lead about half a metre long and terminated in a crocodile clip. If the case is made from a soft plastic the small grommet in the exit hole for this lead is not essential, but will serve to give the unit a neater appearance. The metal prod part of the unit consists of a long M3 or 6BA bolt which is filed to the usual pointed tip. Ideally the bolt should be about 50 to 75 millimetres long, so that it is easy to poke the unit into the less accessible parts of the equipment under test. In practice you might have to settle for a somewhat shorter bolt, since longer ones do not seem to be stocked by electronic retailers. The bolt is fixed at one end of the unit using a suitable nut, and a soldertag is fitted over the bolt inside the case. This provides an easy means of making the connection to the probe tip.

The on/off switch can be fitted on the case anywhere that will keep it out of the way when using the unit. Similarly, the exit hole for the output cable can be positioned anywhere that does not make the unit awkward to handle and use. Probably in both cases the rear end of the unit is the best place for them. The on/off switch needs to be a very small type, and a sub-miniature toggle or slider type should be suitable. The output cable does not need to be a screened type, and any twin cable should be suitable. As the output is at d.c. and a fairly low impedance it is quite in order to use a fairly long cable if desired.

It has to be emphasised that this is only a suggestion for the general make-up of the unit, and it is really a matter of making the most of the materials that are available to you. With a little ingenuity it should be possible to produce a reasonably professional finished unit. A fairly slimline case is preferable to a short stubby type, as a long slim case makes it easier to get the unit into the more inaccessible parts of electronic projects.

Components (Figs 2.2 and 2.3)

R1	10M ¼ watt 5%
R2	1k ¼ watt 5%
R3	220 ¼ watt 5%
C1	470p ceramic plate
C2	4n7 polyester
C3	470n polyester
C4	470p ceramic plate
TR1	BF244B
D1, D2	OA91 (2 off)
D3, D4	BZY88C4V7 4.7V 400mW zeners (2 off)
B1	9 volt (PP3 size)
S1	SPST miniature toggle
	Case, circuit board, battery connector, etc.

High Resistance Probe

The advantage of a d.c. voltmeter which has a very high input resistance was discussed in BP239, but to briefly recapitulate, the limitations of an ordinary analogue multimeter come to

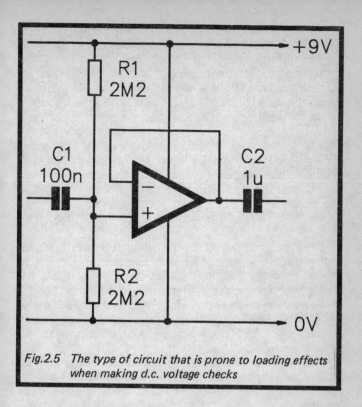

Fig.2.5 *The type of circuit that is prone to loading effects when making d.c. voltage checks*

light when testing a high impedance circuit, such as the bias network in the buffer amplifier of Figure 2.5. This is a standard operational amplifier voltage follower circuit, where the voltage gain from the input to the output is unity. The circuit provides plenty of current gain though, with a low output impedance being produced from what in this case is an input impedance of about 1.1 megohms. R1 and R2 bias the input of the amplifier to approximately half the supply voltage, or about 4.5 volts in other words.

Measuring this voltage with a high impedance voltmeter, such as a digital multimeter having an input resistance of about 10 or 11 megohms, will give reasonably accurate results. The resistance of the multimeter is effectively shunted across R2, and will tend to pull the measured voltage below the 4.5 volt level, but the measured voltage should not be too far from the unloaded voltage at this point.

Making the same measurement with an ordinary 20k per volt multimeter will give a very different result. To measure a nominal potential of 4.5 volts it would seem to be reasonable to use the multimeter on its 5 volt d.c. range, but on this range it provides an input resistance of only 100k (5 x 20k = 100k). This would shunt R2 to such an extent that a very low reading indeed would be obtained. With an inexpensive 1k per volt multimeter the resistance on the 5 volt d.c. range would only be 5k, which instead of giving nearly full scale deflection of the meter, would result in R2 being shunted to the point where the meter's needle would probably not be noticeably deflected!

The circuit of Figure 2.6 is for an input resistance booster that provides any multimeter with an input resistance of 20 megohms on its lower d.c. voltage ranges. The unit is not usable with input voltages of more than about 7 volts, but it is on low voltage readings that a high input resistance is likely to be greatest benefit. With modern semiconductor circuits virtually all voltage readings seem to be in the sub-ten volt range anyway.

The circuit is basically just an operational amplifier used in the unity voltage gain non-inverting mode. R3 and D1 provide protection against excessive input voltages. For positive input voltages D1 is reverse biased, and it acts as a conventional zener diode which avalanches to clip the input voltage at a little over 8 volts. With a negative input voltage D1 becomes forward biased, and clips the input signal at about −0.7 volts, like an ordinary forward biased silicon diode.

R1 and R2 are the input bias resistance for IC1, and they set the input resistance of the circuit. Two 10 megohm resistors in series obviously gives an input resistance of 20 megohms, but it is quite in order to use three or more of these resistors connected in series if desired. For instance, with five 10 megohm resistors an input resistance of some 50 megohms would be obtained, and accurate results should then be obtained even when testing very high impedance circuits.

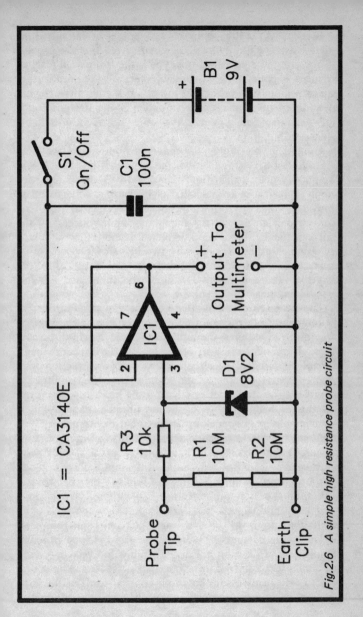

Fig.2.6 A simple high resistance probe circuit

57

IC1 is a CA3140E, which is a type that has an ultra-high input resistance due to its MOS input stage. It is also capable of operating in a circuit of this type without the need for dual balanced supplies. This is possible because the output stage can provide output voltages as low as a few millivolts. The use of an alternative operational amplifier in the IC1 position is not recommended. Very few other types have suitable characteristics.

Using a 9 volt supply the maximum output voltage from IC1 is about 8 volts, and it will be somewhat less than this as the battery nears exhaustion. The CA3140E can operate with supply voltages up to 36 volts, giving output voltages up to almost 35 volts. By using a higher supply potential it is therefore possible to extend the maximum input voltage that the unit can handle, but a supply voltage of more than about 18 volts (which can be provided by two PP3 size 9 volt batteries connected in series) are probably not very practical. Note that the voltage rating of D1 should be about one volt less than the nominal supply voltage.

The circuit is so simple that construction should pose few difficulties. Note though, that IC1 is a MOS input device that consequently requires the usual anti-static handling precautions. In particular, use an holder for this for this component, do not fit it onto the circuit board until construction is in other respects complete, and handle the pins as little as possible. The unit does not have to be built in probe form, but this probably represents the most practical approach. It is vulnerable to stray pick-up at the input due to its very high input impedance (especially if more than two input resistors are used), and because IC1 effectively provides half wave rectification. This will not matter if the unit is constructed as a probe, because a long positive test lead will then be avoided. Pick-up in the short probe tip and wiring should be negligible.

If conventional test leads are used at the input it is quite likely that there will be a strong indication from the meter under no input conditions due to the stray pick-up of mains "hum" etc. One solution, and probably the best one, is to use oscilloscope style screened test leads. These can be expensive to buy ready-made, but do-it-yourself leads of this type can be produced reasonably cheaply. Another alternative would be to add a lowpass filter at the input of the unit, but this would slow up its response time slightly. Note that stray pick-up at the input does not matter when testing low impedance sources since the pick-up will drop to an insignificant level when the unit is connected to the test point. The same is not true when testing high impedance sources, and unless pick-up is kept down to an insignificant level the accuracy of voltage readings will be adversely affected.

The voltage range of the multimeter is, of course, unaltered by adding the impedance booster unit. However, bear in mind the maximum input voltage limitations mentioned previously.

Components (Fig.2.6)

R1	10M ¼ watt 5%
R2	10M ¼ watt 5%
R3	10k ¼ watt 5%
C1	100n ceramic disc
D1	BZY88C8V2 8.2 volt 400mW zener diode
IC1	CA3140E
B1	9 volt (PP3 size)
S1	SPST miniature toggle
	Case, circuit board, 8 pin d.i.l. i.c. holder, battery connector, etc.

Dual Range Booster

Figure 2.7 shows the circuit diagram for an improved voltage probe unit. This is much the same as the original in that it consists of a voltage follower circuit with an overload protection circuit at the input. It is different in that the input bias resistors have been replaced with a simple two step switched attenuator (R1 to R3 plus S1). With S1 set so that R4 connects to the top end of R1 the unit functions in much the same way as the original circuit, but with a reduced input resistance of a little over 11 megohms. This input resistance is obviously still quite good, being comparable to analogue high impedance voltmeters and digital multimeters.

With S1 set to the opposite position the input attenuator reduces the input voltage by a factor of ten. Whereas previously the circuit had a maximum input voltage of around 7 to 8 volts, switching in the attenuator multiplies this to a

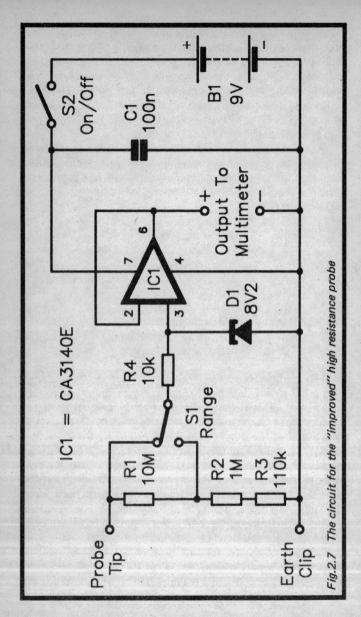

Fig.2.7 The circuit for the "improved" high resistance probe

more useful 75 to 80 volts maximum. It does this without the need for higher supply voltages, and requires the addition of only two extra components (S1 and a resistor) in comparison to the original circuit. Provided a miniature type is used for S1, there should be no difficulty in building the unit as a probe type tool. Note that the attenuator resistors must be close tolerance types in order to give accurate results on both ranges.

In use the unit is not greatly different to the original design. However, bear in mind that when it is set to divide the input voltage by a factor of ten, the actual voltage reading is ten times the figure indicated by the multimeter.

Components (Fig.2.7)

R1	10M 0.6 watt 1%
R2	1M 0.6 watt 1%
R3	110k 0.6 watt 1%
R4	10k ¼ watt 5%
C1	100n disc ceramic disc
D1	BZY88C8V2 8.2 volt 400mW zener diode
IC1	CA3140E
B1	9 volt (PP3 size)
S1	SPDT miniature toggle
S2	SPST miniature toggle
	Case, circuit board, 8 pin d.i.l. i.c. holder, battery connector, etc.

Memory Probe

One of the most common problems when making voltage checks on circuit boards is the difficulty in holding the test prods in position while looking away to read the multimeter. The small size and intricacy of modern circuits makes the job of keeping the test prods in place one that often requires all your concentration, even if you are able to clip the earth lead in place while the tests are made. You need to take due care when making voltage checks on awkward pieces of equipment – it is all too easy to slip with the test prod and short circuit two adjacent contacts. Some lackadaisical testing could soon add a few more faults to the equipment being checked!

A useful but rare feature which aids testing awkward equipment is a memory facility. This can operate in more than one way, but in its most simple form the multimeter holds the highest or last reading until a reset button is operated. If you are testing fixed voltages, you can simply connect the test prods to the test points, remove them, read the voltage from the multimeter, reset the instrument to zero, and move on to the next test. There is a slight flaw in this method of testing in that if the input voltage is slowly varying, this will not be apparent. You will simply get a reading equal to the highest input voltage while the test prods were connected to the circuit under test, or the last reading prior to them being removed, depending on the design of the multimeter. This is not really a major drawback though, as in practice there are very few test voltages that vary slowly. Mostly they are either static or vary at a rate that is too high for the multimeter to cope with. However, it is probably not the technique to use if you are (say) checking for low frequency instability on supply lines, or anything where there is a definite possibility of a slowly fluctuating input voltage.

Although very few multimeters have any form of integral memory circuit, it is not difficult to add this feature using an external circuit. It will only function on the lower d.c. voltage ranges, but these are the ones that are most often used when making "dab it and see" style checks on circuit boards.

A very basic memory circuit can be provided using a passive circuit such as the one shown in Figure 2.8. This relies on the multimeter being a high input resistance type. When an input voltage is connected to the unit, C1 charges up to this input voltage, and when the input voltage is removed it discharges slowly into the high input resistance of the multimeter. The discharge process is very slow due to the high input resistance of the multimeter and the high value of C1. This gives you a few seconds to read the multimeter before the displayed voltage has time to "sag" significantly. Pressing reset button PB1 rapidly discharges C1 through R1 so that a new reading can be taken. R1 provides current limiting so that sparking at PB1's contacts is avoided, and it has a long operating life.

Although this circuit will work, it does have a couple of major deficiencies. One of these is simply that the readings are

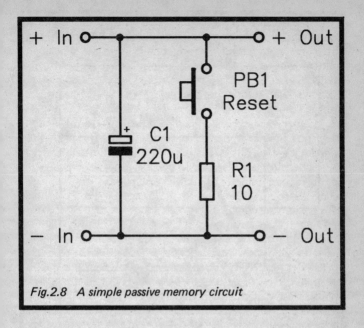

Fig.2.8 A simple passive memory circuit

not held very well. Although the time constant of C1 and the
10 or 11 megohm input resistance of the multimeter is very
long, tests made with a digital multimeter will clearly show the
reading dropping on each update of the meter's display. This
can be a bit confusing, making it difficult to take readings.
The second problem is the high value of C1. This will rapidly
charge if the unit is fed from a low impedance source, but it
could take several seconds or even minutes if the test point
is at a high impedance. This could result in very low readings
and misleading results being obtained. Also, connecting a
high value capacitor to test points involves a slight risk of
damaging components in the circuit. C1 could be made lower
in value, but this would exacerbate the problem of "sagging"
readings. C1 must be given a value that gives a good com-
promise between these two problems.

Vastly superior results can be obtained using an active
circuit, such as the one shown in Figure 2.9. The input part
of the circuit is much the same as the passive circuit of Figure

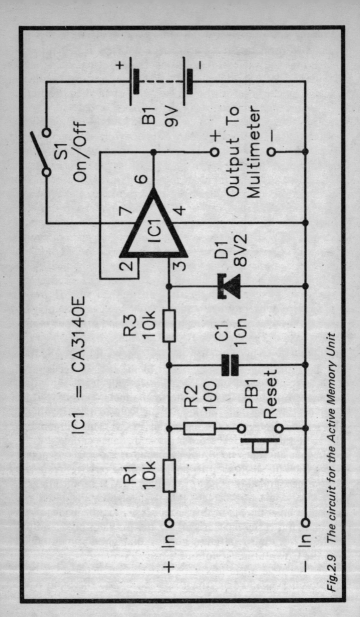

Fig.2.9 The circuit for the Active Memory Unit

IC1 = CA3140E

64

2.8, and works in exactly the same way. It differs in that the value of the charge storage capacitor (C1) has been made very much lower in value at just 10 nanofarads. This is less than a thousandth of the original value, and it ensures that the input voltage quickly rises to the correct level even when the unit is fed from a high impedance voltage source.

The active part of the circuit is an operational amplifier used in the unity voltage gain non-inverting mode. This is much the same as the stage used in some of the previous circuits. It is possible to use such a low charge storage capacitor due to the MOS input stage of the CA3140E used in the IC1 position, and the ultra-high input resistance this provides. The input resistance is about 1.5 million megohms, which ensures that there is no significant decrease in the charge on C1 over a period of a few seconds. In fact the main discharge path for C1 is likely to be through its own dielectric, and the use of a good quality plastic foil type is recommended. The low value of C1 means that there is little risk of it causing any damage to components in the equipment under test. However, R1 provides current limiting that ensures there is absolutely no risk of any charge or discharge currents of sufficient magnitude to damage anything in the test circuit.

D1 provides overload and reverse polarity input protection, as in some of the circuits described previously. Obviously this component provides an additional discharge path for C1, and could degrade the performance of the circuit. In practice this does not seem to be a problem though, and at voltages reasonably well below the avalanche point a zener diode seems to exhibit a very high resistance indeed.

This is another very simple circuit that should be very easy to construct. It could easily be built as a probe, and in use this would probably be the most convenient form for the unit. Bear in mind that the maximum output voltage is about one volt less than the supply voltage. Higher supply voltages can be used in order to increase the maximum possible output voltage, but the 36 volt maximum permissible supply potential for the CA3140E must not be exceeded.

Components (Fig.2.9)

R1	10k ¼ watt 5%
R2	100R ¼ watt 5%
R3	10k ¼ watt 5%
C1	10n polyester or polycarbonate
D1	BZY88C8V2 8.2 volt 400mW zener diode
IC1	CA3140E
B1	9 volt (PP3 size)
S1	SPST miniature toggle
PB1	Push to make — release to break
	Case, circuit board, 8 pin d.i.l. i.c. holder, battery connector, etc.

A.C. Voltage Booster

Although multimeters have few major deficiencies, few are very good at making very low voltage measurements. This is one respect in which digital instruments are generally much better than analogue types, apart from a few high quality analogue multimeters. It is perhaps not so much a problem for d.c. voltage measurements, where most multimeters are somewhat better, and very low d.c. voltage measurements are not something that need to be made very often anyway. The problem is usually more acute when making measurements on audio gear where it is often necessary to make low a.c. voltage checks. Few multimeters, especially analogue types, offer full scale values of less than about 5 or 10 volts. This does not provide particularly good resolution, and makes it impossible to measure potentials of just a few millivolts. In some cases even inputs of a few hundred millivolts can not be measured with reasonable accuracy.

If you have a digital multimeter with 0.1999 volt a.c. and d.c. voltage ranges, then you are fortunate in that you can accurately measure quite small a.c. and d.c. voltages, with a resolution of some 100 microvolts (0.1 millivolts). This is adequate for most audio testing, but the frequency response limitations of most digital multimeters have to be taken into account. With an upper limit to the frequency response of typically about 500 hertz, gain testing etc. can be undertaken provided a suitable test frequency is chosen. Noise measurement and most frequency response testing are not practical propositions using such an instrument. Also, the lack of logarithmic decibel scaling on a digital multimeter makes it less than ideal for much audio testing.

As pointed out in BP239, some audio tests can be undertaken by ensuring that the output level is high enough to properly drive a multimeter set to a low a.c. voltage range. This is a bit risky though, in that there is a real possibility of overloading the equipment under test and obtaining misleading results. Not all equipment can provide a high enough output level to permit this approach to be used successfully. More reliable results and a greater range of tests can be undertaken if the multimeter is preceded by an amplifier to boost its sensitivity. This method is particularly useful if it is applied to an analogue multimeter which has an a.c. voltage range with a full scale value of only about one volt, a bandwidth of 20kHz or more, and decibel scales. Adding a simple and inexpensive amplifier to a multimeter of this type provides you with a setup. that is capable of the type of testing that would otherwise require an expensive a.c. millivolt meter or an oscilloscope.

The Circuit

Figure 2.10 shows the circuit diagram for a simple a.c. voltage booster circuit. The input stage is a simple unity gain buffer amplifier that provides an input impedance of over one megohm (less at high frequencies due to the inevitable input capacitance). This high input impedance alone gives a definite advantage over using an unaided analogue multimeter for low a.c. voltage checks. Most analogue multimeters have a sensitivity of 20k per volt on the d.c. voltage ranges, but the sensitivity is often much lower on the a.c. voltage ranges. It is usually in the region of 5 to 10k per volt. This gives rather low input impedances on the low a.c. voltage ranges (only 10k on a 2 volt a.c. voltage range with a sensitivity of 5k per volt for instance).

The voltage amplification is provided by IC2 which is an operational amplifier used in the standard inverting mode. It has two switched feedback resistors (R6 and R7) which provide voltage gains of 40dB (one hundred times) and 20dB (ten times) respectively. With the multimeter switched to

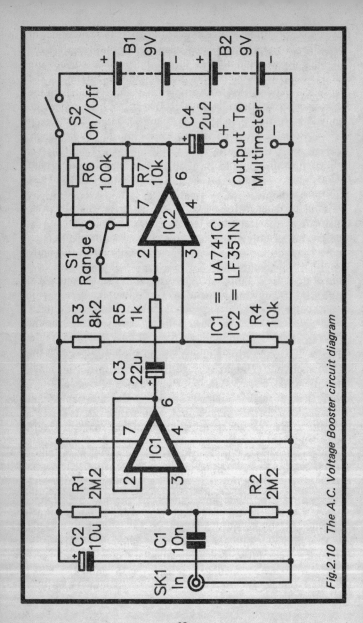

Fig.2.10 The A.C. Voltage Booster circuit diagram

68

(say) the 2.5 volt a.c. range this would give full scale values of 25 millivolts and 250 millivolts r.m.s. Note that these are the full scale values, and that it should be possible to measure voltages of around one millivolt reasonably accurately. The theoretical bandwidth of the amplifier is about 400kHz in the X10 mode, and 40kHz in the X100 mode. In practice the bandwidth might be slightly less than these figures, but even so, the unit still encompasses more than the full audio range. The limiting factor might be the bandwidth of the multimeter, but most analogue types seem to have a frequency response that extends at least as far as the 20kHz upper limit of the audio spectrum.

Power is obtained from two 9 volt batteries wired in series to give an 18 volt supply. This enables an output of up to about 5 volts r.m.s. to be obtained. In order to obtain accurate results right up to the full scale value, the multimeter must therefore be switched to a range having a full scale value of 5 volts or less. Most multimeters have a suitable range, but a few have a 10 volt range as their lowest a.c. voltage type. With instruments of this kind they should either be used at output voltages of less than 5 volts, or a higher supply voltage should be used. The maximum permissible supply potential is 36 volts, which gives a maximum unclipped output voltage of around 11 volts r.m.s. If the multimeter has a 1 or 1.5 volt a.c. voltage range, then it will almost certainly be possible to obtain satisfactory results with the unit powered from a single 9 volt battery. The current consumption is only a few milliamps, and PP3 size 9 volt batteries are adequate as the power source.

Constructing this unit is a little more difficult than building the circuits described previously in this chapter. The unit is still pretty simple, but as it has a high input impedance and a fair amount of voltage gain it is necessary to be reasonably careful with the component layout if instability is to be avoided. As the input and output of the circuit are out-of-phase, problems with stray feedback are minimised, but reasonable care with the layout still needs to be taken. In order to avoid problems with stray pick-up of mains "hum" etc., it is a good idea to fit the unit in a metal case earthed to the negative supply rail.

The test leads must be of the screened variety so as to minimise stray pick-up and to minimise the risk of problems with instability. Obviously there is no need to use a screened lead to connect the output of the unit to the multimeter in order to avoid stray pick-up. The signal in the output cable is at a relatively high level and low impedance. However, using a screened output lead is probably a good idea as it keeps down any radiation of the output signal to an insignificant level, which aids the avoidance of problems due to stray feedback.

Components (Fig.2.10)

R1	2M2 ¼ watt 5%
R2	2M2 ¼ watt 5%
R3	8k2 ¼ watt 5%
R4	10k ¼ watt 5%
R5	1k 0.6 watt 1%
R6	100k 0.6 watt 1%
R7	10k 0.6 watt 1%
C1	10n polyester
C2	10μ 40V elect
C3	22μ 25V elect
C4	2μ2 63V elect
IC1	μA741C
IC2	LF351N
SK1	3.5mm jack socket or similar
S1	SPDT miniature toggle
S2	SPST miniature toggle
B1	9 volt (PP3 size)
B2	9 volt (PP3 size)
	Case, circuit board, 8 pin d.i.l. i.c. holder (2 off), battery connector (2 off), etc.

Gain Estimation

In use the system is suitable for many applications that would conventionally be the province of an a.c. millivoltmeter or an oscilloscope. These include such things as gain measurement, noise measurement, and frequency response testing. Some types of audio testing are covered towards the end of BP239, including frequency response testing and audio output power measurement. These can both be checked using the setup described here, but the higher sensitivity achieved with the amplifier added enables measurements to be made at lower levels than would otherwise be possible.

The measurement of voltage gain is an important part of audio testing, since a loss of gain in an audio circuit is a common result of a fault. Quickly tracking down the stage which has inadequate voltage gain can obviously make finding the exact problem much easier and faster. The basic method of checking is to inject an audio signal at a suitable level into the input of the equipment, and to then check the signal level at various points in the circuit. If there is a total or very substantial loss of signal at some point in the unit, then locating the faulty stage is not likely to be too difficult. You could, for example, make tests at the input and output of every stage in the circuit working from the input to the output. When a point in the circuit with an inadequate level is located, the fault is in the immediate vicinity of that point, and is probably just prior to it.

Very often the problem is not a total break in the signal path, or even a large loss of gain. The loss of gain is frequently only around 10dB (about 3 times) to 30dB (about 30 times). When testing for these lower levels of signal loss you need to be able to judge the sort of voltage gain that each stage should be providing. The problem might be obvious, because a stage of amplification might be providing losses rather than gain. On the other hand the problem could be a less obvious one with, for example, an amplifier that should be providing 50dB of voltage gain actually providing only about 20dB of gain.

Transistors have three basic amplifying modes, and the basic circuits for each of these are shown in Figure 2.11. The configuration shown in (a) is the common collector mode, which is better known as the "emitter follower" mode. It is easy to spot this type of amplifier as it is the only one which has the output signal coming from the emitter. There is no difficulty in working out the voltage gain of an emitter follower — it is always fractionally less than unity. This type of amplifier is used as an impedance converter to match a high impedance source to a low impedance load.

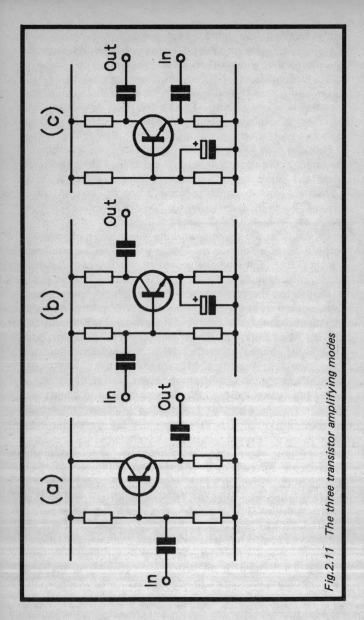

Fig.2.11 The three transistor amplifying modes

72

The configuration of (b) is the common emitter mode, and is probably the one that is used most frequently. The voltage gain of this mode is quite high, but the precise figure varies considerably depending on the component values and the current gain of the transistor. With low gain transistors the voltage gain is still likely to be in excess of ten times, and with high gain types such as the BC107 and BC547 series the voltage gain would normally be over one hundred times.

Modern common emitter stages often use a more simple form of biasing which has the emitter connected direct to the earth rail and the two base bias resistors replaced with a resistor connected between the base and collector terminals. This provides a certain amount of negative feedback, but does not massively reduce the voltage gain of the circuit. What does produce a large loss of gain is the unbypassed emitter resistor which is sometimes included to provide local negative feedback. In some cases there is a single resistor and no bypass capacitor in the emitter circuit. In other cases there are two resistors with a bypass capacitor connected across one of them.

As a quick "rule of thumb", the voltage gain is approximately equal to the value of the collector load resistor divided by that of the unbypassed emitter resistance. This gives quite accurate results unless the unbypassed emitter resistance is quite low in value (about 100 ohms or less). The problem is that there is effectively some emitter resistance within the transistor that must be added to the external resistance. As this internal resistance is typically only about 25 ohms, it is often not large enough to affect the calculation significantly. However, if the emitter resistance is quite low in value, the voltage gain of the stage will be slightly lower than the method of calculation described above would suggest.

The configuration of (c) is the common base mode. This is little used in audio circuits, but it is sometimes used as part of the so-called "longtailed pair" configuration. This is basically just an emitter follower stage directly driving a common base amplifier. The input impedance of this type of stage is low, and it is sometimes used as the input stage of a circuit that requires a low input impedance (such as certain types of microphone preamplifier). There is a moderate

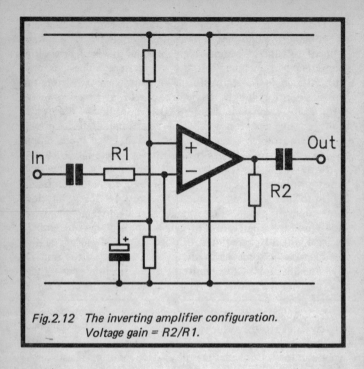

*Fig.2.12 The inverting amplifier configuration.
Voltage gain = R2/R1.*

amount of voltage gain through this type of circuit, which provides an action that is a bit like a step-up transformer.

Accurately judging the voltage gain of audio amplifier stages that are based on operational amplifiers is a somewhat easier task than dealing with discrete transistor based circuits. There are two basic modes of operation, which are the inverting mode of Figure 2.12, and the non-inverting mode of Figure 2.13. In the inverting mode the non-inverting input is biased to about the mid-supply level by a potential divider circuit. A negative feedback circuit comprised of two resistors connects between the output, the inverting input, and the input. These are resistors R1 and R2 in Figure 2.12, and their value sets the voltage gain of the amplifier. It is delightfully simple to calculate the voltage gain. Simply divide the value of R2 by that of R1.

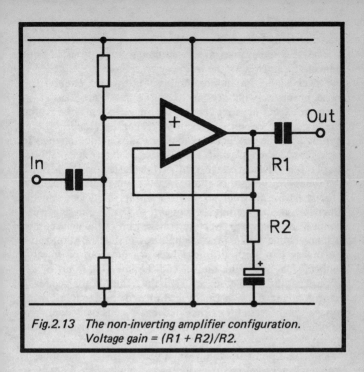

*Fig.2.13 The non-inverting amplifier configuration.
Voltage gain = (R1 + R2)/R2.*

The non-inverting circuit is similar, but the input signal is coupled to the non-inverting input. The feedback network connects between the output, the inverting input, and the earth rail. The mathematics of the circuit's voltage gain are a bit different with this configuration. The voltage gain is equal to the values of R1 and R2 divided by the value of R2. If the ratio of R1 to R2 is quite high, simply dividing R1 by R2 will give a reasonably accurate answer.

Both configurations are frequently used with capacitors in the feedback circuit in order to give a contoured frequency response. This technique is often used in tone controls and R.I.A.A. preamplifiers for instance. This complicates matters as in order to work out the voltage gain you must first calculate or look-up the reactance of each capacitor at the test frequency, then work out the effective feedback resistances.

It is probably more practical to simply check that the appropriate type of frequency response is being produced, and to assume that the stages are functioning correctly if nothing seems to be amiss with the frequency response.

Stages based on audio amplifier integrated circuits can cause problems when trying to "guesstimate" voltage gains. Some or all the negative feedback components may be within the integrated circuit. The popular LM380N audio power amplifier device is a good example of such a component. In these cases the relevant data book or data sheet should supply the typical voltage gain of the device, which is 34dB (50 times) in the case of the LM380N. Some audio integrated circuits have one feedback resistor within the device and the other one as an external component, so that the designer can exercise some control over the voltage gain of the device. For instance, some audio power amplifiers in the TBA800 series use this system, with an internal resistor of about 6k in value connected between the output and the inverting input of the amplifier. Provided you can find the value of the feedback resistor in the data on the device, or perhaps graphs showing voltage gain versus external feedback resistor value, you should be able to work out the correct voltage gain for the circuit.

One final point to watch when gain testing is that there is no overall negative feedback loop which will affect the voltage gain through each stage. With power amplifiers and discrete preamplifier circuits, it is not unusual to have several stages connected in series, with overall negative feedback to set the closed loop voltage gain accurately at the required figure. Stages which provide unity voltage gain will still do so with overall negative feedback applied, but those that provide voltage gain will produce less than normal due to the feedback. This presents no real problem provided you spot the overall feedback and take it into account. In fact a lack of gain through one stage will probably be partially counteracted by increased gain through another stage, making the lack of gain in the faulty stage stand out more clearly.

Current Tracing
Tests on circuit boards tend to be in the form of voltage rather

than current tests, since the latter can only be made if a break is made in the signal path so that the meter can be connected into it. There are actually some expensive pieces of equipment which measure current flow using a Hall Effect device to measure the magnetic field around the wire which carries the current, but these are quite expensive and are probably not a practical proposition for the home constructor. There is a more simple alternative, and although it is quite crude by comparison it can nevertheless provide some quite useful results.

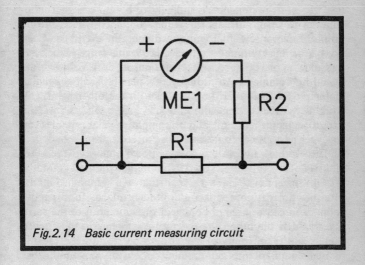

Fig.2.14   Basic current measuring circuit

This alternative system is really just a variation on the standard current meter arrangement. The basic current measuring setup is shown in Figure 2.14. It consists of a resistor through which the current to be measured must pass (R1), plus a voltmeter to measure the voltage developed across the resistor (ME1 and R2). Ohm's Law dictates that the voltage across the resistor is proportional to the current flowing through it. Although the meter is actually measuring the voltage across the resistor, it can therefore be calibrated directly in terms of current flow.

In a simple current tracing setup a dual test prod with the prods separated by a few millimetres is used. This is connected to a length of copper track on the printed circuit board, or onto a component leadout wire. In effect, the piece of copper track or leadout wire between the two prods acts as the resistor of the current meter. By measuring the voltage developed across the two prods a good idea of the current flow through the track or wire is obtained.

The problem with this arrangement is that the resistance through a short piece of copper track or leadout wire is extremely low. Even with a fairly high current of an amp or two, the voltage obtained is unlikely to be more than a millivolt. With small currents the voltage obtained is likely to be no more than a few microvolts, and could be even less. Even using a digital multimeter on its 0.1999 volt range (which has a resolution of 100 microvolts) it is unlikely that usable results would be obtained. An ordinary 20k per volt analogue multimeter plus a high gain d.c. amplifier on the other hand, will work very well in this application. Figure 2.15 shows the circuit diagram for an add-on amplifier that enables an analogue multimeter to be used as a current tracer.

This is basically just a conventional full-wave precision rectifier of the type often used in audio millivoltmeter circuits. It is not essential to have a circuit that will respond to inputs of either polarity, but it is a definite advantage. In this application you can not simply connect one test prod to the earth rail and dab the other one onto various points in the circuit, thus ensuring an input of the correct polarity. The tracking of many modern printed circuit boards is so convoluted that the polarity of the signal carried by each track might not be immediately obvious. The only slight drawback of this method is that you can not determine the polarity of the current flow using the unit, although it would seem unlikely that it would ever be necessary to do so. An advantage of using a dual polarity circuit is that the unit should be able to detect a.c. signals as well as d.c. types, but the limited upper frequency response means that it will only operate efficiently at frequencies of a few hundred hertz or less.

The circuit is a form of operational amplifier inverting mode amplifier. IC1 is a small monolithic voltage regulator

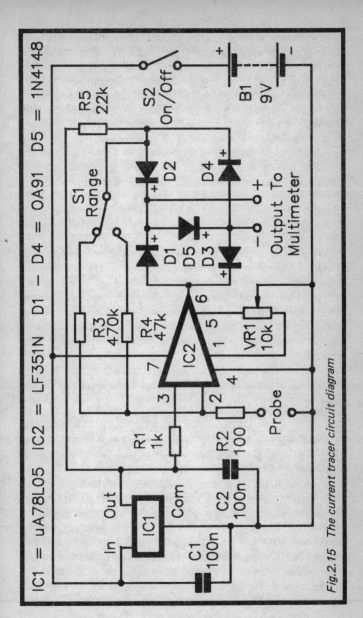

IC1 = uA78L05 IC2 = LF351N D1 – D4 = OA91 D5 = 1N4148

Fig.2.15 The current tracer circuit diagram

that provides a stable bias potential of 5 volts to the non-inverting input of IC2. It also provides what is effectively the mid-supply earth rail. The meter circuit is driven from between this pseudo-earth and the output of the amplifier by way of a bridge rectifier (D1 to D4) and series resistor R5. R2 plus R3 or R4 forms the negative feedback network, and controls the voltage gain of the circuit. Having two switched feedback resistors provides the unit with two sensitivities, with R3 offering approximately ten times more gain than R4. As the rectifier circuit is included in the feedback loop it tends to counteract the non-linearity through the diodes, giving better results. Germanium diodes are used for D1 to D4 because their lower voltage drop makes them more suitable for this application than the more common silicon diodes such as the 1N4148.

D5 is used to protect the meter against severe overloads. If a strong output signal should be produced, D5 will become forward biased and will clip the output voltage at about 0.65 volts. This should prevent any damage to the multimeter, which should be switched to the 50 microamp d.c. current range. VR1 is the offset-null control. With a theoretically perfect operational amplifier this control is unnecessary. Real operational amplifiers tend to fall short of theoretical perfection in a number of ways, and one result of this is small voltage differences between the inputs and the output. These are multiplied by the closed loop voltage gain of the amplifier, and with the high gain that has to be used in this application the result is a strong positive deflection of the meter under standby conditions. VR1 enables the offset voltage to be trimmed out, and the meter to be properly zeroed under quiescent conditions.

Construction of the unit should once again be quite simple. Although the circuit has a substantial amount of voltage gain, its low input impedance plus the fact that the input and output are out-of-phase means that instability is not a major problem. VR1 can be an ordinary panel control, or a preset resistor on the main circuit board. Using a panel mounted control has the advantage that it can easily be retrimmed from time to time should it prove necessary to do so (which it probably will). If this component is a preset resistor it should be a multi-turn type as the resolution of many ordinary preset resistors is inadequate for this application. Using a multi-turn "trimpot" has the advantage of making the critical adjustment of VR1 much easier.

There are two approaches to the test prods for this unit. One is simply to use a pair of ordinary multimeter type test prods, which you place a few millimetres apart on the track or wire being tested. This is the method I prefer as it is simple, and it permits the test prods to be positioned as far apart as the length of track or lead permits. This gives the best possible input signal to the unit. The disadvantage is that by using an inconsistent track or wire length it becomes more difficult to interpret results. You must learn to take into account the length of track or wire used when assessing results. This is not too difficult, since the effective sensitivity of the unit is proportional to the length of track or wire used. The second method is to fix the two prods together so that the metal tips are a few millimetres apart. This brings the advantage of a consistent gap between the prods, and only one hand is needed to manipulate them. The drawback is that a quite small gap must be used if the unit is to be usable on any track or wire. This gives a relatively low input signal, and effectively reduces the sensitivity of the unit.

When first switched on it is unlikely that any offset will be apparent, and the meter should be properly zeroed. This is due to the fact that with no input signal connected to an inverting mode operational amplifier circuit its effective voltage gain is unity. If you place a short circuit across the test prods, this will place the circuit under normal operating conditions, and a strong deflection of the meter will probably result. VR1 is adjusted to accurately zero the meter, and it will almost certainly need to be adjusted very carefully in order to achieve this. Carry out this adjustment with the unit on its more sensitive range (S1 set to switch R3 into circuit), as it is on this range that there is the largest offset.

The only way to master a unit of this type is to experiment with it on a circuit that is operating correctly, and where you know the approximate current running through each track. This will give you a good idea of what to expect when testing faulty equipment. In many cases the current flows in faulty areas of equipment are so far removed from the correct figures that there is no difficulty in detecting them. The sensitivity of the unit should be adequate, but low currents may not give a significant deflection of the meter. You can obtain increased voltage gain by making R2 lower in value. This reduces the input impedance of the unit, but as the source impedance is so low this should not result in significant loading of the test voltage. The main problem is that the higher the sensitivity is made, the more difficult it becomes to zero the meter using VR1, and the more prone the circuit becomes to drifting of the bias levels. It is perhaps worthwhile experimenting with lower values for R2 to see if this gives acceptable stability, and it is worthwhile using a lower value if results are acceptable in this respect.

Components (Fig.2.15)

R1	1k ¼ watt 5%
R2	100R ¼ watt 5%
R3	470k ¼ watt 5%
R4	47k ¼ watt 5%
R5	22k ¼ watt 5%
VR1	10k lin potentiometer or multi-turn preset
C1	100n disc ceramic
C2	100n disc ceramic
IC1	µA78L05 +5 volt 100mA regulator
IC2	LF351
D1	OA91
D2	OA91
D3	OA91
D4	OA91
D5	1N4148
S1	SPDT miniature toggle
S2	SPST miniature toggle
B1	9 volt (PP3 size)
	Case, circuit board, 8 pin d.i.l. i.c. holder, battery connector, control knob, etc.

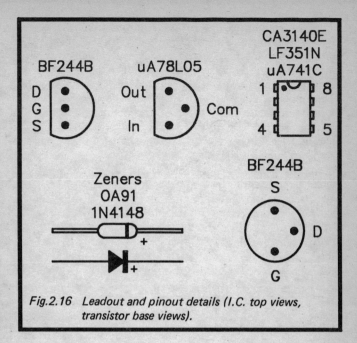

*Fig.2.16   Leadout and pinout details (I.C. top views,
           transistor base views).*

Please note following is a list of other titles that are available in our range of Radio, Electronics and Computer books.

These should be available from all good Booksellers, Radio Components Dealers and Mail Order Companies.

However, should you experience difficulty in obtaining any title in your area, then please write directly to the Publisher enclosing payment to cover the cost of the book plus adequate postage.

If you would like a complete catalogue of our entire range of Radio, Electronics and Computer books then please send a Stamped Addressed Envelope to:—

BERNARD BABANI (publishing) LTD
THE GRAMPIANS
SHEPHERDS BUSH ROAD
LONDON W6 7NF
ENGLAND